D-DAY
TO BERLIN

D-DAY TO BERLIN

Armour Camouflage and Markings
of the United States, British and German Armies,
June 1944 to May 1945

Terence Wise

ARMS AND
ARMOUR

Published in Great Britain by
Arms and Armour Press,
Villiers House,
41-47 Strand,
London WC2N 5JE.
A Cassell imprint.

Distributed in the USA by Sterling Publishing
Co. Inc., 387 Park Avenue South, New York, NY
10016-8810.
Distributed in Australia by Capricon Link
(Australia) Pty. Ltd., 2/13 Carrington Road,
Castle Hill, NSW 2154.

British Library Cataloguing in Publication Data:
Wise, Terence
D-Day to Berlin.
1. Armoured vehicles, Military 2. Vehicles, Military-
Camouflage 3. Vehicles, Military-Markings 1. Title
355.8'3 UG446.5

ISBN 1-85409-212-X

Colour artwork by John W. Wood & Associates.
Artists: John W. Wood, William Hobson, Jack
Pelling, David E. Smith.

Acknowledgment
The author wishes to acknowledge the valuable
assistance rendered by Steve Zaloga and Bruce
Culver, who read the U.S.A. and German sections
of the manuscript, and who gave criticism and
offered advice which enabled a better book to be
produced. Whilst benefiting from this advice, the
author did not always agree with their opinions, and
any errors in this work must therefore remain
entirely his responsibility.

Edited by Michael Boxall.
Designed by Anthony A. Evans.
Printed and bound in Singapore by Craft Print Ltd.

Overleaf: Vehicles of 20th Armoured Division,
XV Corps, waiting for a pontoon bridge to be
completed across the Danube in the Zirgesheim
area of Germany, April 1945. The nearest
Sherman bears a white star as well as a name and
serial number, but the Shermans beyond do not
appear to have stars on their turret sides. Note
the layers of thick dust on the upper surfaces.
(U.S. Army)
Opposite; Sd Kfz 251 in two-colour sprayed
camouflage of dunkel gelb and olivgrun, with
staining, dust and mud, and the front and sides
heavily camouflaged with evergreen foliage, in
the Ardennes, December 1944. (I.W.M.)

Contents

Introduction
The Principles of Camouflage

To understand the art of camouflage, it is first necessary to understand the principles of visibility. An object is seen because it is in contrast to its background: this contrast may be in shape, shadow or texture, colour, shine, tone or movement, or any combination of these. Regularity of shape will also identify an object; shadow will reveal the shape of an object far better than its own outline. Texture, which depends on absorption or reflection of light by a surface, gives a rough or smooth appearance to objects and affects the tone of their colour. Colour contrast can distinguish one object from another alongside it. Shine reveals position and possibly identity; and movement attracts attention. The main factors that were used in the art of camouflage to overcome these principles are listed below.

For concealment from ground forces, a background was chosen which virtually absorbed the object without changing the appearance of that background more than was necessary. From the air, land takes on a patchwork appearance; regular for cultivated land and built-up areas, broken and haphazard for natural areas. Care had to be taken to avoid disturbing this pattern.

Any activity would change the appearance of the surrounding area and had to be avoided as much as possible; a vehicle might be invisible from the air yet have its position revealed by its tracks. In Normandy, the Germans employed special teams to sweep away all signs of such tracks.

Foliage could be very effective against both ground and aerial observation, and the writer has experienced the peculiar sensation of seeing a column of vehicles approach to within thirty yards of his tank (camouflaged with branches and positioned at the side of a track junction) which remained undetected until the order to open fire was given at that range.

Evergreens provided the best camouflage because they lasted longer without wilting, but care had always to be taken to see that the foliage used matched the immediate surroundings. Foliage also had to be used the right side up; the upper surfaces of most leaves are waxy and considerably darker than the undersides, and foliage used incorrectly could reveal instead of concealing.

Both sides made extensive and successful use of foliage in north-west Europe, but because of their great air superiority, the Allies were able to carpet-bomb areas where vehicles were known to be hidden, and under such massive aerial bombard-

Left: An aerial view of U.S. tanks advancing through hedgerows west of St. Lô. This is a good illustration of the bocage country, where foliage was to play an important part in concealment. Note the tell-tale tracks, so revealing of position when hiding from aerial attack. (I.W.M.)
Opposite page: Counter-shading principles **1.** Top surfaces darkened; **2.** Darkening extended over edges to conceal the shape of these surfaces; **3.** Shadow of truck on the ground is extended up the lower edges of the vehicle to break these edges and distort the shadow; **4.** Unless catching the sun, windows stand out as black shapes which need to be broken up by the application of dark paint round the edges.

ment, no form of camouflage could be effective.

Garnished nets, either employing tape or natural foliage, were also used a great deal to disguise the shape of vehicles. These nets were particularly effective in static positions, when poles could be used to push the net up and out to form an irregular shape.

The use of paint on vehicles for camouflage purposes is our prime concern here, but it should always be remembered that paint, by itself, did not give complete camouflage and was really most effective on fixed installations: paint has no texture of its own, and texture is one of the major factors in successful camouflaging.

It was common practice in all the armies covered by this book, to paint all vehicles and equipment in a single basic colour. Because the textured surface of the ground looks darker from the air, these overall colours had to be several shades darker than the terrain, and the British, in particular, used black paint extensively on the upper surfaces of their vehicles. A good example of this basic principle is an aircraft on a runway. If both are light coloured, the aircraft is made conspicuous by its shadow: if a light coloured aircraft is placed on a dark runway, or vice versa, the aircraft is picked out by the contrast with

its surroundings: place a dark aircraft on a dark runway and the problem is solved.

Camouflage patterns were applied over the basic colour in a contrasting colour or colours to break up the vehicle's distinctive outline. One of the principles which governs the form and position of these patterns is known as counter-shading, a technique employed to counteract shade and shadows or reflected light. This technique was developed to prevent vehicles being identified by the shape of their shadow, and by their various surfaces being picked out in different shades, because of the angle and different light-reflecting properties of those surfaces. To reduce this natural reflection and shadow outline, paint was applied to blur the outlines, i.e. dark paint on surfaces reflecting the most light, light paint on surfaces in shadow. The best example of this is a six-sided pencil, held up to a light source. Of the three sides visible to the holder, the side nearest the light source will be light, the side farthest away will be dark, while the third side will be somewhere between the two. By darkening the light surface and lightening the dark, it is possible to make these three sides 'flatten' into one surface.

The accompanying drawing of a lorry shows some of these counter-shading

techniques. Note particularly the method of dealing with glass, which was always a danger because of its great reflecting potential. The Germans tried to camouflage such areas with tape, the Americans with a film of oil which attracted dust, and both used fold-down windscreens with covers. It should also be remembered that many a would-be Rommel revealed his position because the goggles pushed up on his head formed a perfect reflecting surface.

The actual shape of the patterns varied considerably from army to army and, in the German Army especially, from vehicle to vehicle. The basic principles were that regular outlines, regular spacing and symmetrical shapes should be avoided—they are not found in nature—and the patterns should be bold.

Although such patterns appear effective at ground level, their value in fact is limited, and they did not give absolute prevention of identification either from the ground or from the air. However, they had the advantage of making the type of vehicle difficult to identify from the air (and aircraft were seeking the tanks), while at ground level they reduced visibility by attracting attention to the individual shapes rather than the whole object and so helped to confuse the enemy's aim.

The U.S. Army

For the reasons mentioned in the Introduction, the U.S. Army chose a matt olive drab as the most satisfactory overall colour for blending with all the various terrains in which U.S. Army vehicles could be expected to serve. Exceptions had to be made to this general rule, of course: for example, in snow covered areas; for such vehicles as fire fighting and crash tenders, which were painted red; and buses, sedans, rear echelon ambulances and the like, which used a gloss olive drab because it was more hard wearing and concealment was not the prime objective.

The overall olive drab was first used on vehicles in 1941 and remained in use as the basic camouflage colour throughout the war. The U.S. Corps of Engineers official specification number for the colour was 319, more usually referred to as Olive Drab No. 9. The official paint chips show No. 9 to have been exceptionally dark, whereas in most photographs studied it appears to be considerably lighter. There are a number of reasons for this discrepancy: a fine coating of dust over the paint; a fading of the original shade due to exposure to wind, rain and sun; the wear and tear of active service, for which a matt paint was not ideally suited so far as durability goes; but principally because of an optical effect known as scale distortion, whereby a shade of paint invariably appears to the human

Below: M4A3E8, prototype for the M4A3 (76mm) HVSS, test-firing in France, March 1945. The tank is painted overall olive drab, but is heavily marked with dust, mud and scratches. Note unit codes on rear: 12△-X HQ15. (U.S. Army)

U.S.A. 3032131

Opposite page, top: M8 armoured cars, M3 half-tracks and jeeps of Company A, 23rd Infantry, 7th Armored Division, near Epernay, France, August 1944. The vehicles are all in overall olive drab. (U.S. Army)

Opposite page, bottom: An M15 of 712th Armored, 90th Infantry Division, on the heights of the old château at Château Thierry, August 1944. The half-track is in overall olive drab, but note discoloration at the door and how the flaps at the rear take on a different shade because of their angle. (U.S. Army)

Top: A half-track of the 540th Engineers, 36th Division, towing a 57mm anti-tank gun, landing at San Raphael, southern France, August 1944. A broad pattern has been painted on this vehicle in field drab over the olive drab. (U.S. Army)

Middle: Men of the 84th Engineer Camouflage Battalion, attached to 100th Division, Seventh Army, spraying an M5A1 tank near Montbronn, France, March 1945. (U.S. Army)

Bottom: An M16 quadruple AA on M45 half-track passing through the village of Waldweisse, Lorraine, in late 1944. The gun shield and trailer tarpaulin (side) have been painted with an individual pattern, but the remainder of the vehicle appears to be in olive drab only. The jeep is also in olive drab; note how the two vehicles appear to be painted in different shades because of the angle at which the light strikes the various parts of the vehicles. The unit codes have been censored, but these vehicles belong to 3rd Armored Division. (U.S. Army)

Top: Tanks and lorries of a Free French unit at Utah Beach, August 1944. All vehicles are painted olive drab, with fresh markings. The hatches are also olive drab (see bottom right). Note size and position of stars on cab roofs of softskins, and on upper surfaces of AFVs. (U.S. Army)

Left: M8 armoured cars of 4th Armored Division passing through Le Repas, France, early August 1944. All vehicles are olive drab, marked with dust and stains. The open hatches are also olive drab on the under surfaces. (U.S. Army)

Opposite page, top: An M7 manned by Free French of 5th Division Blindée, French First Army, Keysersberg area, France, December 1944. The olive drab is covered with dust and mud, and the suspension also carries a good deal of earth. (U.S. Army)

Opposite page, middle: M7 of 2nd Division Blindée, Free French Forces, in action in France, 1944. The olive drab is again covered in stains, dirt and dust, and the suspension coated with mud. (U.S. Army)

Opposite page, bottom: 155mm of 991st Field Artillery Battalion, in action near Kornelmunster, Germany, November 1944. Again, the vehicle is covered with earth and dust. (U.S. Army)

eye to be darker on a small area than it does when applied to a large surface. Tests with the official chips show that when held against a painted vehicle the shades match perfectly, but when that vehicle is viewed from a distance the paint appears to be of a lighter shade.

In October 1942 new instructions were issued for the camouflage painting of vehicles. Under these instructions olive drab remained the overall colour but was now to be broken up by the use of Field Drab No. 4 (specification number 303) in temperate zones, with black paint used on the top surfaces and bottom edges of vehicles. The other new colours, introduced for other climatic areas, do not concern us here, although Earth Red No. 8 (specification number 312) was used on rare occasions in north-west Europe in three-colour painting.

Strict instructions were issued for the use of this three-colour system of painting, with definite patterns suggested for the various types of vehicles. However, it was not recommended that every vehicle within a unit be painted in exactly the same pattern, and local commanders were merely instructed to follow the basic idea of the official patterns, keeping to bold and simple patterns for maximum effect. The colour plates show some of these basic patterns; others may be seen less clearly in some of the photographs. The principles which governed these patterns have been described in the Introduction.

Vehicles were painted in overall olive drab before leaving the factory but the pattern painting was to be done by the Engineer Camouflage Battalions in the various theatres of operations: tank crews received only tins of olive drab for the repainting of worn areas. The camouflage manuals, paints, and spray equipment were therefore in the hands of these rear echelon units, which spent most of their time camouflaging depots and field artillery positions, and very little time painting tanks. In fact, it would appear from battalion records that only one such battalion spent any significant time on tank pattern painting, though others occasionally passed some of the paints to the armoured units for the crews to do their own pattern painting. This is borne out by photographic evidence: the hard edges on almost all vehicle camouflage patterns studied by the writer indicate that the contrasting paints were applied mostly by brush, not by spray gun.

In some Commands no camouflage patterns were applied and the vehicles remained in overall olive drab. This was most noticeable in armoured units, where the vehicle casualty rate was high and the crews in any case relied more heavily on foliage than paint for camouflage. Also,

Left: An M4 of First Army at a road junction in Hurtgen Forest, November 1944. The olive drab has the typical 'chalky' appearance of the basic colour in the field, while the external gear and heavy coating of mud are also typical for this time of year. The large white 'B' on the turret is part of a tactical sign for identifying vehicles within a squadron or regiment. (U.S. Army)

Bottom: M25 tank recovery tractor of 134th Ordnance Battalion, 12th Armored Division, towing a Sherman in Rahlingen, France, December 1944. Both vehicles are painted olive drab, and both are fairly dirty, but note how the tank appears to be a lighter shade, particularly on the hull, presumably because of a heavier layer of dust. (U.S. Army)

Opposite page: A T34 multiple rocket launcher on M4A3, 134th Ordnance Battalion, 14th Armored Division, XXI Corps, Seventh Army, Fletrange area of France. The olive drab shows as the light shade frequently seen on active service vehicles, dusty and heavily stained. (U.S. Army)

the camouflage painting of tanks was generally considered to be a very low priority so far as the tankmen themselves were concerned. Statistics for equipment losses underline why many armoured vehicles remained in overall olive drab: equipment replacement figures in north-west Europe were as high as 500 tanks, 2,400 vehicles and 100 artillery pieces per month. Softskins, which were more vulnerable, relied more on pattern painting, particularly in the case of the forward echelons.

However, some armoured formations *did* use painted patterns to camouflage their tanks, usually as a result of local instructions. For example, the 2nd Armoured Division, which landed in Normandy in the late afternoon of D-Day, was for several days held in the rear in anticipation of a breakout. The divisional commander utilised this time to have the vehicles painted with camouflage patterns, using rear elements around him to assist in the task. Heavy losses around St Lô whittled down the number of vehicles in this pattern painting, and there is no indication from photographic evidence that replacement vehicles received similar treatment.

The canvas tilts of trucks, jeeps and such like vehicles were provided by the manufacturers in an olive drab colour. Inevitably this meant a number of different

shades, which did not necessarily match the official olive drab. The textured surface made the canvas appear a darker shade than it actually was.

On armoured vehicles the underside of hatches were painted olive drab so that they would not be conspicuous in their normal open position. The interiors of open vehicles, such as jeeps and scout cars, were also painted overall olive drab.

During the summer and early autumn of 1944 in France, most vehicles were inevitably covered in a fine layer of dust. This in itself formed a natural camouflage, as did the mud of late autumn and winter, and of early spring in 1945. Mud was most abundant on the wheels and suspension and helped to 'black out' these areas, but it was also splattered up the sides and rear of vehicles, either by their own wheels or tracks or by those of passing vehicles. The combination of olive drab paint, dappled by dried or drying mud, made a very effective camouflage, and on rare occasions mud was deliberately daubed on vehicles by the crews, usually only on the softskins.

Another natural camouflage was foliage, and the crews of the tanks appear to have gone to great lengths to make full use of this excellent camouflage aid. For example, it was common practice to rig wires round vehicles to provide places into which branches and twigs could be thrust,

Opposite page, top: An M29 armoured carrier at an ordnance depot during the winter of 1944-45. The carrier is olive drab, but has picked up a thick layer of mud. (U.S. Army)

Opposite page, middle: An M4 of 5th Armoured Division, French First Army, passing through Hericourt, November 1944. The tank is well camouflaged with evergreen foliage and its suspension is thickly coated with mud. (U.S. Army)

Opposite page, bottom: An M8 HMC (75mm howitzer) with Cullin Hedgerow Device, at Barenton, France, August 1944. Foliage has been used to break the outline of the vehicle. Note the various shades of the olive drab along the side. The '3-9' is a local tactical sign. (U.S. Army)

Top: Shermans of 2nd Armored Division in the Frandeux area of Belgium, December 1944, using wire netting to secure evergreen foliage to the turrets—the tank nearest the camera has this extended over the hull. No markings are visible. (U.S. Army)

Middle: Knocked-out M4 of French 2nd Armoured Division near the Moselle River, September 1944. This, and the other tank, are using foliage over the olive drab. (U.S. Army)

Bottom: T34, early spring, 1945. The vehicle's snow camouflage is wearing off the frequented areas. The glacis has been reinforced with sandbags, held in position by welded rods supporting wire mesh. This, and the similar arrangement on the hull side, show clearly how foliage was attached. (I.W.M.)

although most vehicles already had a fair number of useful crevices. Even more popular was chicken wire, which was wrapped round the turret, and occasionally even round the gun barrel, to provide purchase for dozens of small branches. Quite a few Shermans also had rods welded horizontally along the hull sides, with the chicken wire fastened to these rods: the rods were usually welded on by the Ordnance crews responsible for maintenance and repair, often on instructions from battalion or even divisional commanders.

Softskins do not appear to have used such devices and did not make such extensive use of foliage. They did, however, use camouflage nets to some extent—normally only when stationary—whereas American AFVs do not in the main appear to have favoured nets, probably because of the inevitable problems of snagging on external fittings and keeping the turret clear for traverse. An official U.S. publication on the subject of nets is of the opinion that ungarnished large mesh nets had absolutely no camouflage value, and states that the smaller mesh nets, *as supplied to AFVs*, were designed for use without garnish, although they benefited from the addition of local leaves, scrub etc.

Vehicle outlines, particularly in the case of AFVs, were also broken up by the common practice of carrying a large

Opposite page, top: Shermans of 747th Medium Tank Battalion in Schleiden, Germany, January 1945. The right hand tank has had two inches of armour and three inches of air space added by welding track plates to the turret and hull sides and to the glacis. The other tank appears to have sandbags on the glacis; both AFVs are swathed in metal mesh as a camouflage aid. Note how the barrels have had much of the dust layer removed, probably because they provide a convenient hand-hold when mounting and dismounting. (U.S. Army)

Opposite page, bottom: Vehicles and equipment of First Army concentrated for the crossing of the River Roer, February 1945. Nets were used extensively in such situations to prevent discovery by enemy aircraft. (I.W.M.)

Top: Vehicles of French 2nd Armoured Division en route to France. All are in U.S. olive drab, but this photo shows a predominance of nets—rigged on the trucks for use when mobile—which was unusual in American formations. Note the method of displaying the aerial recognition star on the windscreen covers of the jeeps. (I.W.M.)

Right: An M4 (105mm howitzer) of 3rd Battalion, 66th Armored Regiment, 2nd Armored Division, near Amonines, Belgium, in January 1945. Because of their static position in open terrain, these AFVs are making use of nets. Note the dapple effect on the side of the nearest vehicle, caused by dirt on the olive drab paintwork. (U.S. Army)

Opposite page, top: A Sherman of 48th Tank Battalion preparing for action near Hatten, France, in January 1945. Netting has been used here on both the turret and glacis. The condition of the paintwork, including the serial number and Allied stars, due to wear, dirt and exposure, is well worth noting. (U.S. Army)

Opposite page, bottom: An M7B1 (105mm howitzer) in support of 101st Airborne Division at Bastogne, in late 1944. The olive drab has a chalky appearance and is heavily stained with dirt, washed off in places by rain or snow. The marks around the howitzer are probably oil stains. The obliterated code is '10 △ 423(?)', making this the 12th vehicle of Company C, 423rd or 420th Armored Artillery Battalion, 10th Armored Division. The rolled camouflage net on the glacis is also coated with dirt. (U.S. Army)

Top: Infantry and supporting tank destroyer, manned by Free French, outside Colmar, January 1945. The AFV is heavily laden with gear which makes identification difficult. It bears a tricolour device on the hull side. Snow camouflage has been applied, but it was either applied partially or has worn off. (U.S. Army)

Left: Shermans of a Free French armoured division passing through Dijon during November 1944. All are in olive drab, marked with dust, and cluttered with gear. (U.S. Army)

amount of gear externally; haversacks, helmets, bedding rolls, water or petrol cans, and tarpaulins cluttered the exterior of many vehicles, as may be seen from the photographs. This was not officially encouraged (it could cause fire if hit by incendiary or HE rounds) and was mainly for the convenience of the crew. It is doubtful if this practice improved the vehicle's camouflage, but it certainly made identification of the type of vehicle much more difficult.

Tank destroyers and Shermans also made a common practice of 'reinforcing' their armour with sandbags on the hull front, and less often round the turret and/or hull sides. Most often the sandbags on the glacis were roped or wired in place. Some bags do not appear to be lashed and these were probably sacks of concrete or cement which solidified and adhered to the glacis of their own accord. The bags round turret and hull sides were usually held in place by webbing straps, though some vehicles had a metal framework welded to the turret and/or hull sides to hold them in position; again, this would have been done by the Ordnance crews.

The 1942 regulations had stipulated camouflage painting for snow areas as precise patterns of white and black, or white and olive drab, and when the first snows came in the winter of 1944-45 some U.S. Army vehicles were camouflaged accordingly. However, the snows coincided with the last great German offensive

Top: An M4A1 (76mm) HVSS on the outskirts of Innsbruck on 3 May, 1945. The tank's armour is reinforced by sandbags, held in place by welded metal strip and rods. (U.S. Army)

Middle: Two early M4s of 14th Armored Division, Seventh Army, knocked-out in Lohr, April 1945. The sandbags on the nearest AFV are held in place by metal strip, welded to turret and hull. (I.W.M.)

Left: A Sherman of Company A, 701st Tank Battalion, Ninth Army, in Brachelen, Germany, January 1945. An overall coat of whitewash has been applied, even over the tow-rope and some tools on the rear, but not on the suspension. (U.S. Army)

Opposite page, top: An M8 armoured cars in Germany, January 1945. Although both are from the same unit, the whitewashed vehicle is from Company C, the other from HQ. Note how the stars and unit codes have been left unobscured. (U.S. Army)

Opposite page, bottom: Shermans of 40th Tank Battalion, 7th Armored Division, First Army, firing on enemy positions beyond St. Vith, January 1945. A thick coat of white paint has been applied and this has been aided by a fall of snow, the remains of which coat the upper surfaces of the AFVs. Note the staining by petrol on the second vehicle, the application of paint over the netting on the hull of the nearest tank, and the combination of snow and paint on the wheels and suspension. (U.S. Army)

Top: An M8 HMC (75mm howitzer) at Bastogne, December 1944, using white sheeting for snow camouflage while halted. (I.W.M.)

Left: A two-and-a-half ton truck of 6th Armored Division during the winter of 1944-45, using foliage and a tarpaulin to conceal its position whilst static. A fall of snow has greatly assisted this simple camouflage. (I.W.M.)

Opposite page, top: An M8 armoured car in late January 1945. The olive drab has been white-washed for winter, and snow lays on the glacis, but wear and weather has taken much of the whitewash off again. Note the whitewash on the undersides of the hatches. No unit identification is visible except 'R-52' on the left mudguard, which also bears the name 'Kansas Terror'. (U.S. Army)

Opposite page, bottom: A Sherman of 753rd Tank Battalion, 36th Infantry Division, in overall white camouflage, with what looks like a distinct overspray of black—though this could be just the olive drab showing through. (U.S. Army)

of the war, in the Ardennes, and in the front line particularly a variety of hurried and improvised methods were used. Most often this consisted of hurried sploshing or daubing of whitewash or white paint over the existing paintwork, with varying amounts of the original paint remaining visible: little or no effort appears to have been made to follow any recognisable patterns. The wheels and suspension were not usually treated this way, remaining olive drab with normally a good coating of mud or dirt.

In the Ardennes a few instances occur of white sheeting being used over vehicles which had not been painted white, while others, in overnight static positions, used their tarpaulins to break the vehicle outline and relied on a snow fall to cause a 'white out'. The camouflaging of all vehicles was improved by snow falls, of course, and such snow was usually left in situ, primarily because of the crews' reluctance, in cold and dangerous conditions, to clear the snow off areas other than entry points, rather than as a deliberate attempt to use the snow as a means of breaking the vehicle outline and providing a white 'coat'.

As the thaws came, mud again splattered up on to the white paint, which in any case was showing signs of wear and tear: as winter receded so the vehicles graduated naturally towards a more olive drab-mud coating. In the pine forests of Germany this olive drab and white, or more official black and white, was sometimes improved by painting criss-crossing black 'sticks' on the white areas. This followed one of the official camouflage painting patterns (illustrated in the colour plates) but does not appear to have been widely used: no examples of it on tanks have been seen by the writer, though it does occur occasionally on half-tracks.

Opposite page, top: An M4 of 5th Armored Division, French First Army, in the streets of Colmar, February 1945. Much of this tank's whitewash has worn off and, as the snow thaws mud has also splattered up the rear of the lower hull. (U.S. Army)

Opposite page, bottom: An M16 AA half-track of 457th AA Artillery Automatic Weapons Battalion, near Canach, Luxembourg, during February 1945. This vehicle has been roughly white-washed, although much of it has worn off, and the bodywork seems to have been rubbed to remove traces of it. (U.S. Army)

Above: Calliope in action in Beisdorf, Germany, February 1945. This AFV has been whitewashed, but some has worn off, and is also using foliage to match its immediate surroundings. (U.S. Army)

Right: A half-track of 28th Infantry Division in the town of Balgau, three miles from the Rhine. Whitewash has been splattered over the olive drab to give an effective snow camouflage. A darker 'stick' pattern appears to have been painted over this—note left rear—but it is not clear. (U.S. Army)

Tod den Zerstörern Europas

National identification and aerial recognition marks

Several different forms of white, five-pointed star were used during the Second World War as national identification marks in the various theatres, but in the spring of 1944 some uniformity was achieved for the invasion of France by the introduction of the plain white star for use on vehicle sides and the white star within a white circle for use on upper surfaces as an aerial recognition sign. The star and circle was also used sometimes in a position where it might be either for aerial recognition or national identification, or both; for example on the glacis of tanks.

Where these signs might become covered, such as when a jeep's windscreen was covered and/or folded down on to the bonnet, or the canvas tilt was folded back, it was customary to also paint a star on the area thus exposed, or on a rectangle of canvas which could then be tied over the top. Softskins normally had the aerial recognition sign on the cab roof if the body had a canvas tilt, and on the bonnet if the cab had a canvas top, but the bonnet was the most popular site on most vehicles.

The size of these stars was mainly limited by the space available on the various types of vehicle, but it did not officially exceed 36 inches nor measure less than six inches between opposite points. Table 1 lists some common sizes and locations: it should be remembered that the stars were not always painted in *all* the positions indicated and experienced tank crews frequently painted out the stars on hull front and sides because they provided good aiming marks for German anti-tank gunners.

Table 1. Sizes and locations of identification stars

Vehicle	Location	Size (inches)
Jeeps	sides	6
	front bumper	6
	top of hood	20
¾, 2½ and 5 ton trucks	front and rear	6
	cab doors	16
	top of hood	20
APCs	front and rear	10
	sides	16
	top	20
Tanks	rear (2)	12
	turret top	16
	turret sides	20
	front of glacis	20

As a result of Allied air units attacking their own forces in Sicily, vehicles for the north-west Europe campaign also carried rectangular panels of fluorescent acetate, referred to as 'colours of the day'. The colour was changed daily, and the appropriate panel displayed on the top of the vehicle. There seem to have been panels of three different colours, the colour chosen for the coming day being released with other codes on the preceding evening.

Opposite page, top: An M3 half-track of HQ, XX Corps, near Thionville, France, in January 1945. This is a rare example of the use of a dark pattern on whitewash, in this case by the application of a dark paint, possibly black, over the olive drab. (That it is not the original coat of olive drab is confirmed by the repainting of the serial number and the paint extending on to the tyres.) The chalk lines, drawn to guide the whitewash painter, can still be seen. Note the rough application of the whitewash, and how the tools and chain have also been covered. (U.S. Army)

Opposite page, bottom: A Sherman of a Free French unit with Seventh Army in action in Marseilles, August 1944. It bears the Free French national insignia on the rear, as well as tactical markings, and the Allied white star on the turret side. (U.S. Army)

Top: An M7 crossing a temporary bridge in Remiremont, France, in September 1944. The star on the vehicle's side may be in red, in which case it is a most unusual example, or it may merely have been painted out with fresh olive drab, which would illustrate the difference between new paint and old paint faded by exposure and wear. (U.S. Army)

Bottom: An M18 in action in Wiesloch, Germany, in April 1945. This tank destroyer carries stars in the official positions on glacis and turret side, but has an extra, smaller star on the turret bin. Unit codes identify it as a vehicle of Company C, 824th Tank Destroyer Battalion, 100th Division of VI Corps, Seventh Army. (U.S. Army)

All vehicles also officially carried 'U.S. ARMY' in three-inch high letters in the following positions: trucks, on both sides of the bonnet and truck body and across the tailboard; AFVs, both sides and rear on the most appropriate surfaces. On AFVs with hulls, such as SP guns and APCs, the legend was repeated on the front.

On most softskins this simply meant the legend was painted two inches above the registration number, but in some cases it was used as a prefix to that number, when it was often abbreviated to 'U.S.A.'

Unit codes

The identification of units within the various armies was achieved by codes of numerals and letters which were normally painted on the front bumpers and tailboards of softskins, and on the glacis and hull rear of tanks. These codes may be divided into four classes: Army, Corps and Division; Regimental or Battalion; Company; and individual vehicles. Normally only division, regiment, company and vehicle codes would be carried at the tactical level.

Army codes consisted of the army's number in Arabic numerals followed by an 'A' for army: Corps codes were the Corps number in Roman numerals followed by 'AB' if Airborne or △ if Armoured: and the Division code was the division number in Arabic numerals followed by 'AB' if Airborne or △ if Armoured.

Regimental and Battalion codes followed the same pattern, i.e. the number of the regiment or battalion (or detached company) followed by the branch of service symbol, as in Table 2.

Table 2. Regimental and battalion codes

AA	Anti-Aircraft	M	Medical
AB	Airborne	—O*	Ordnance
△	Armoured	P	Military Police
APH	Amphibious	Q	Quartermaster
C	Chemical	S	Signals
E	Engineer	T	Transportation
F	Field Artillery	TD	Tank Destroyer
—I*	Infantry		

*These letters were always preceded by a half inch dash to prevent confusion with the numerals.

Right: An M7 of 6th Armored Division undergoing repairs at Brulange, France, in November 1944. The bottom points of the star on the glacis can just be seen beneath a layer of mud and the logs across the vehicle's front. The unit codes appear in the most common position for the M7, and read (backwards) seventh vehicle of Company C, 276th Field Artillery Battalion, Third Army. (U.S. Army)

Below: M4A3 (105mm) tanks laying down a barrage from a French wheat field, July 1944. Their white stars have recently been painted out (note the different shades of paint) but they still carry the serial numbers. (U.S. Army)

Where a unit had no intermediate organisation, such as in an HQ unit, then the letter X was used.

Company codes also consisted of a letter for the company (or troop or battery) followed by 'HQ' if a headquarters unit, 'SV' if a services unit. Companies operating independently also carried a special code (see Table 3).

Table 3. Company codes

AM	Ammunition
AW	Automatic Weapons
CON	Construction
DP	Depot
DS	Direct Support
GAS	General Automotive Maintenance
GS	General Support
HW	Heavy Weapons
MR	Mortar
MT	Maintenance
PM	Parachute Maintenance
R	Reconnaissance
RP	Repair
TMP	Transportation Motor Pool

Each vehicle within a company, troop or battery was also assigned a number in the sequence in which that vehicle would normally appear in the order of march. Thus 1-10 were normally allocated to the HQ unit of a company, 11-20 to the vehicles of the 1st Platoon, 21-30 to the vehicles of the 2nd Platoon, and so on.

Table 4. Examples of vehicle numbering within a company

2 -67	C-10	10th vehicle of C Company, 67th Tank Battalion, 2nd Armoured Division
82AB-X	HQ61	61st vehicle HQ unit of 82nd Airborne Division
5 -46	A-4	4th vehicle of A Company, 46th Armoured Infantry Regt., 5th Armoured Division
3A-61Q	A-10	10th vehicle, A Company, 61st QM Battalion, Third Army

Registration numbers

These consisted of a prefix number indicating the type of vehicle, and a number indicating the sequence in which the vehicle had been issued. The prefix letter 'K' was used by the Signal Corps to designate special vehicle types; the letter 'S' after a registration number indicated that the vehicle had been equipped with radio interference suppression. The prefix numbers are shown in Table 5.

The registration numbers, and the 'U.S. ARMY' legend mentioned earlier, were painted in a pale blue-grey at the factories in the United States because at a distance the numbers then merged into the olive drab so as to become virtually invisible. The large number of vehicles with white

Table 5. Registration number prefixes

Vehicle type	Number
Trailers	0
Maintenance trucks	00
Cars and sedans	1
Kitchen trailers	10
Trucks to 1 ton	2
Recce trucks and buses	20
Medium trucks to 1½ tons	3
Tanks and some 'specials'	30
Trucks 2½ to 4-5 tons	4
Tracked and half-tracked vehicles except tanks	40
Trucks over 5 tons and prime movers	5
Fire and crash tenders	50
Motorcycles including m/c combinations	6
Armoured cars and special technical vehicles	60
Ambulances	7
Amphibious vehicles	70
Wheeled tractors	8
Tankers	80
Full and half-tracked tractors	9

registration numbers seen in wartime photographs are mainly a result of the build-up in England prior to D-Day, much painting being done in England using white paint instead of blue-grey.

On softskins the numbers were painted in three-inch high numerals on both sides of the bonnet and body, and across the tailboard. On AFVs they were on each side and the rear of the vehicle. AFVs also frequently carried the number across an appropriate surface on the front of the hull.

Below: Men of 5th Armored Division with their M10 tank destroyer in Dreux, France, during August 1944. It carries the Allied white star in the normal position for this type of AFV, the 'C 32' being a local tactical sign. (U.S. Army)

M32 tank recovery vehicle in France, June 1944, painted in overall olive drab but with a bold pattern in field drab painted over it. The tiny Stars and Stripes on the hull side was probably the work of a patriotic crew member, for it was not used as a national identification mark in north-west Europe.

M3A1 scout car in France during the summer of 1944, its overall olive drab painted over with a black pattern.

Dodge 4 x 4 weapons carrier in France, summer 1944, painted in the basic olive drab but with field drab pattern painting on both the vehicle and the canvas tilt; the latter was unusual on U.S. Army vehicles, the canvas usually being left as manufactured. Note that the registration number is in light blue, not the white so often seen on vehicles from the U.K.

Dodge 4 x 4 ambulance in France, summer 1944. The vehicle is in overall olive drab and bears the red cross and U.S. Army Medical Corps' insignia.

The British Army

The British Army used several different camouflage colour schemes during the course of the Second World War, not only because of the needs of different theatres and changes brought about by the improving art of vehicle camouflage, but also because it employed vehicles manufactured in the U.S.A. and Canada, which were not supplied in the British colours. Therefore, during the 1944-45 campaigns in north-west Europe there were a number of camouflage colour schemes in use, and it is necessary to deal here with both the British scheme in operation in 1944-45 and the one which preceded it but which was not entirely superseded.

As in the U.S. Army, all vehicles were painted in a basic overall colour: until at

Below: Cromwells preparing to move off for an attack east of the River Orne, mid-July 1944. (I.W.M.)

GMC 6 x 6 2½-ton cargo truck in France during the summer of 1944. On this vehicle, the basic olive drab has been heavily over-painted with black, notably on the top surfaces and lower edges, and a thin streak of field drab has been added to the latter. The markings identify the truck as the 35th vehicle of Company B, 13th Q.M. Battalion.

Willys MB 'jeep' in France, August 1944. This command recce vehicle is in olive drab overall, including the exposed interior. The canvas tilt, shown folded down, is of a similar shade.

M18 tank destroyer (Hellcat) as seen in Brest during August 1944. The Hellcat is painted overall olive drab. (The original studied was heavily coated with dust.) Markings shown include registration number, vehicle name and pin-up, and bridge classification number.

M24 light tank (Chaffee) in France, late 1944. The basic olive drab has been over-painted with whitewash (which on the actual example had flaked off considerably), and all markings, including the Allied white star, have been obliterated by this winter camouflage. The Chaffee was used in recce squadrons from late 1944 onwards.

M7 Priest in France, late 1944. The olive drab basic camouflage colour has been roughly but effectively painted over with whitewash for the winter, almost obscuring the geometrical tactical sign.

M29 armoured carrier (Weasel) in north-west Europe during the winter of 1944-45. No markings appear to have been used on this vehicle. The overall olive drab has been heavily smeared and coated with damp mud.

Sherman M4A3 tank in the Colmar area, February 1945. Whitewash has been applied in a haphazard but highly effective snow camouflage pattern over the olive drab. Note that neither the Allied white star nor the tactical markings remain visible.

M3A1 half-track personnel carrier in the Rhine area, February 1945. The winter camouflage illustrated here consists of a white main coat, with black pattern-painting to break up the upper and lower edges, edged with olive drab, and a 'stick' pattern in black over the white parts. This type of camouflage was not common, but was used with success in the forest areas during the winter of 1944-1945.

least late 1943 this was a matt dark earth. This was over-painted with matt black camouflage patterns which followed the basic principles of camouflage, i.e. black on the areas which could be seen from above (top of body roof or tilt, cab roof, wings and bonnet) with random areas of black on the remainder of the vehicle to help break its outline. A supplement to the current Vehicle Markings pamphlet, notified in Army Council Instructions (ACIs) of 20 October 1943, shows this matt dark earth colour, with the black over-painting having a foliage pattern, i.e. with irregular edges. Dappled and dry-brush patterns had also been recommended as official patterns in the Military Training Pamphlet No. 46, Part 4a (Painting of Mechanical Transport) issued in 1941, and it is probable that these also remained in effect at this date.

The first signs of the changes being made for D-Day occur in early 1944. On 12 January another amendment to the Vehicle Markings stipulates that "Pattern painting as laid down in Military Training Pamphlet No. 46, Part 4a and Camouflage Chart No. 15 will not apply". It goes on to say that some vehicles at present painted green (an olive colour in use prior to the introduction of dark earth) should remain in this colour until repainting was necessary. Soon afterwards, the 1942-43 instructions were withdrawn and there is no indication in the ACIs that new instructions were ever issued. Of course, this was part of the security clamp down for D-Day.

The Public Records Office has in its index a publication entitled *Camouflage Training 1944-53*, but this will not be released for public inspection until 1984 because of the 30 year rule. However, it is obvious that these instructions were the ones which replaced those withdrawn in early 1944, and we know what the new camouflage colours and system were, both from photographic evidence and from people's experience in the army during the 1944-53 period.

In these 1944 instructions, the basic overall colour was changed to khaki drab, which was very similar to the pre-1943 colour, but with more of a brown tone instead of a yellow one. So we have for D-Day some vehicles in this new khaki drab, others in dark earth, possibly a few remaining in the pre-1943 olive green, plus the U.S.A. and Canadian vehicles in olive drab. All these basic colours were subject to variations caused by application, dilution, exposure to wear and tear and the elements, as described in the previous section on the U.S. Army. New vehicles were sprayed with these overall colours at the factories, older vehicles being repainted in the current colour by the

Opposite page, top: A Sexton SP 25pdr of 56th Infantry Brigade, 50th Division, during the Normandy Landings, D-Day plus 1. This Canadian-built vehicle may be in olive drab, or may have been repainted in khaki drab; it is impossible to tell from a black-and-white photo. The markings show that it belongs to 147 (Essex Yeomanry) Field Regiment R.A. ('1177' on hull) with 50th Division ('TT' sign). (I.W.M.)
Opposite page, bottom: Shermans of the East Riding Yeomanry, in late June 1944. All are in an overall colour, probably khaki drab. The tactical signs are in red, edged with white. Note the undersides of the hatches are in the same overall colour. (I.W.M.)
Top: Army vehicle park, November 1944. The lorry in the foreground is in the pre-1943 colours and pattern painting; the light patch on the bonnet is gas-sensitive paint. In the background, the Quads and Standard car are in the Mickey Mouse ear pattern. (I.W.M.)
Bottom: A 15cwt Bedford MWD 4 × 2 G.S. truck, illustrating the precise pattern known as Mickey Mouse ear, applied in black over the khaki drab. (I.W.M.)

M26 Pershing tank in Germany during the last months of the war. The tank is in overall olive drab and bears the Allied star on its turret and hull front (the latter of the circled type). (The actual vehicle studied bears the codes 2 -67 C10 on its hull front.) The bridge classification, '54' in black on a yellow circle, is also on the hull front, below the left hand part of the unit code.

T34 rocket launcher (Calliope) on an M4, Germany, March 1945. By this date many U.S. vehicles were relying heavily on foliage for camouflage, and T34s and Sherman tanks were frequently seen as illustrated. No markings are visible, but this vehicle belonged to the 80th Division.

M4A3 HVSS Sherman tank in Germany, March 1945. The camouflage paint is olive drab, but is largely obscured by dust and the sandbags used to supplement the tank's armour; a typical method of improving the armour of U.S. AFVs.

M4A3 Sherman in Munich, June 1945. The overall olive drab has been mottled with a pattern in dark green. It is not known for certain that patterns of this nature were in use before the end of the war, but it seems likely.

Ford 15cwt, as seen on the Normandy beaches in June 1944. It is in overall khaki drab with black pattern painting and, on the left wing, bears the formation sign of the Royal Netherlands Brigade (Princess Irene's). The serial number ('114') on a red/blue arm of service flash, is on the front of the right mudguard and identifies the vehicle as being part of the brigade's artillery component.

White scout car belonging to the 1st (Motor) Battalion, Grenadier Guards, in France early in the summer of 1944. The Guards Armoured Division formation sign can be seen clearly on the left wing, while the serial number ('54') on a red arm of service flash identifies the vehicle as belonging to the motor battalion of an armoured division.

Tetrarch light tank of the 6th Airborne Recce Regiment, 6th Airborne Division, in Normandy, June 1944. It has been painted khaki drab with black pattern painting over, and bears the formation sign used by both the 1st and 6th Airborne Divisions. The arm of service flash is in the distinctive paratroop maroon.

Quad artillery tractor (Morris-Commercial C8 Mk III) in France during 1944. The khaki drab has been over-painted with the pattern painting referred to as 'Mickey Mouse Ear'. Note the double bridge classification number on the yellow plate, to indicate classification of both the gun and the tractor.

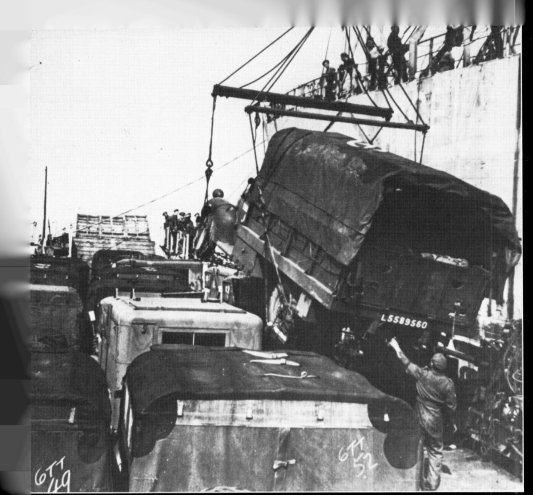

Left. Vehicles of the Princess Irene (Royal Netherlands) Brigade, part of Canadian First Army, loading for France. The two lorries in the immediate foreground carry Mickey Mouse ear over-painting on their tilts, but the lorry being hoisted has the earlier, irregular pattern. Note also the various shades of paint. '6TT49' and '6TT52' are shipping numbers. (I.W.M.)

Bottom: The only sign by which to identify these vehicles, bound for France on D-Day, is what appears to be a white horse and rider on the vehicle named 'Rene' in bottom left. This is probably the formation sign of VIII Corps. Most vehicles and their tilts are in a basic overall colour, but the radio vehicle in the centre foreground and other vehicles to the right and centre, have black pattern painting which is neither Mickey Mouse ear nor the pre-1944 type. This bolder pattern was common in post-war years and was, I suspect, the main type of pattern painting in 1944-45, Mickey Mouse ear being an unnatural variant which did not survive active service conditions. (I.W.M.)

Opposite page, top: D-Day: troops receiving their pay! The sole value of this photo is the bold pattern painting on the tailboard of the lorry—definitely not Mickey Mouse ear, nor one of the pre-1944 patterns. (I.W.M.)

Opposite page, bottom: O.P. carrier of 185 Field Regiment (Glos.) R.A. near Goch, February 1945. The vehicle has the black wavy pattern painting that is typical for carriers. The sign consisting of a white square with a dark circle cannot be identified. (I.W.M.)

Morris-Commercial C8/P, which towed the 17pdr anti-tank gun, as used in France during 1944-45. The khaki drab basic colour has been broken by Mickey Mouse Ear pattern painting in black.

Universal carrier being used as an observation post in the Falaise area, August 1944. The basic khaki drab has black pattern painting in the distinctive wavy pattern seen on many carriers. Although no markings are visible here, this particular vehicle in fact carries 'RE' in white on its side; the serial number '174' on an artillery arm of service flash on the right wing; and the formation sign of 21st Army Group on the left wing. The bridge classification, '5', is on the hull front.

Dingo scout car (Daimler) as used in north-west Europe by the Guards Armoured Division, whose formation sign it bears. The serial number '53' on a red arm of service flash indicates that it belongs to the third armoured regiment of the division. Mickey Mouse Ear pattern painting has been used over the khaki drab.

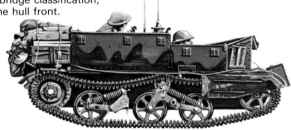

AEC medium artillery tractor (Matador) as used in France during 1944. The khaki drab basic camouflage has been over-painted with Mickey Mouse Ear pattern painting.

Bedford QLT 3-ton lorry, France 1944, also in khaki drab and Mickey Mouse Ear pattern painting. This type of camouflage painting was much more prevalent on softskins than on AFVs.

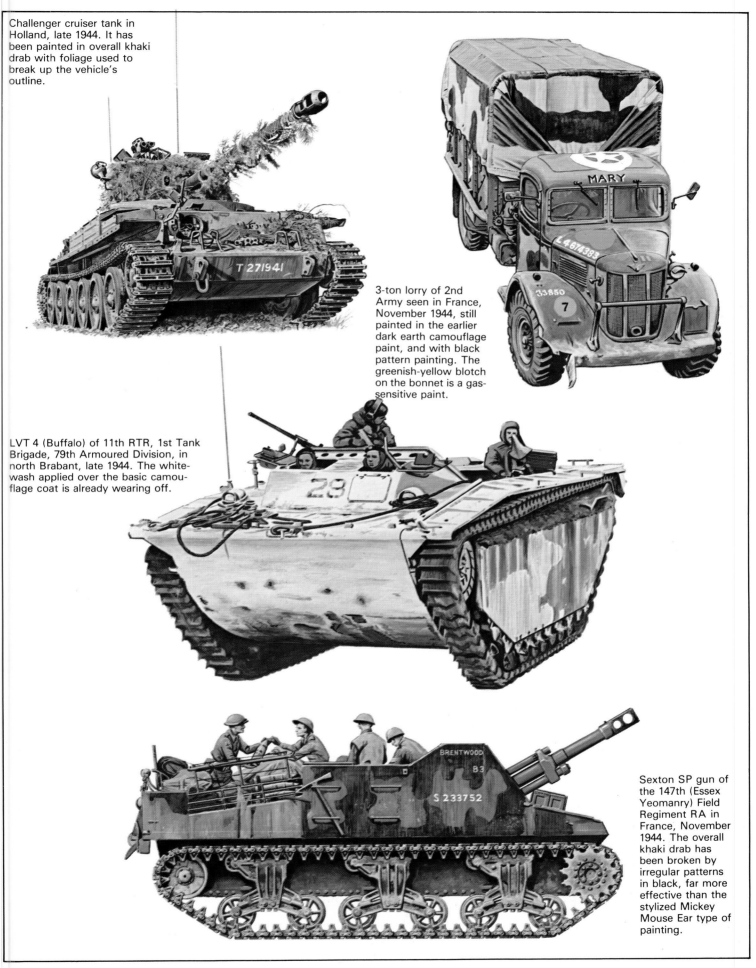

Challenger cruiser tank in Holland, late 1944. It has been painted in overall khaki drab with foliage used to break up the vehicle's outline.

3-ton lorry of 2nd Army seen in France, November 1944, still painted in the earlier dark earth camouflage paint, and with black pattern painting. The greenish-yellow blotch on the bonnet is a gas-sensitive paint.

LVT 4 (Buffalo) of 11th RTR, 1st Tank Brigade, 79th Armoured Division, in north Brabant, late 1944. The white-wash applied over the basic camouflage coat is already wearing off.

Sexton SP gun of the 147th (Essex Yeomanry) Field Regiment RA in France, November 1944. The overall khaki drab has been broken by irregular patterns in black, far more effective than the stylized Mickey Mouse Ear type of painting.

crews or Services as repainting became necessary.

Early in 1944, the camouflage patterns were also changed to the system which has now become known as 'Mickey Mouse ear'. This consisted of large areas of matt black, looking rather like cumulus cloud and formed by painting a number of inter-joined circles of varying diameters. Again, the black paint was applied to all top surfaces, with extensions down onto the vehicle sides, and along the bottom edges of the vehicle. Some vehicles also had individual areas on their sides, formed from three or four interlinked circles. In the 1944 pattern, the underside of the chassis was also painted black.

This black paint was quick drying, and was applied freehand with a brush at an army depot, either by soldiers or by civilian employees. The older patterns will have been replaced by the crews as repainting became necessary. It is interesting to note that by the time this system was cancelled in 1953, the pattern no longer resembled the Mickey Mouse ear, but was of a bolder pattern with fewer curved edges, and these having much greater radii. Such patterns may be seen on vehicles during the 1944-45 period, but until the documents are released we shall not know if this was a different interpretation of the 1944 patterns or merely paintwork performed under the 1943

instructions which had survived subsequent changes. Of course, these bolder patterns conformed more to the principles of good camouflage than did the precise patterns of the Mickey Mouse ear style, and are again being employed by the British Army on its vehicles.

One exception to the Mickey Mouse ear pattern was the bren gun carrier, which normally appeared in the type of bolder, more wavy lines just described. It would seem that this was an official pattern for this type of vehicle, though some do appear in photographs using the Mickey Mouse ear pattern.

Where dark earth remained the overall colour, or where the black paint was

Above: Sherman of 4/7 Dragoon Guards, 8th Armoured Brigade, XXX Corps. The pattern painting is not Mickey Mouse ear, but the bolder style. Note what appears to be a board on the bedding at the rear: this bears a wireless call sign, used as a tactical sign, which looks like '69' in white outline. (I.W.M.)

Left: Shermans of 4th Armoured Brigade east of Goch, February 1945. The evergreen branches along the tanks' sides are typical for this date; but note, more particularly, the paint lightened by dust and dried mud and the heavy mud layer on wheels and suspension. (I.W.M.)

Opposite page, top: AEC Matador near Roermond in the Netherlands, November 1944, painted in Khaki drab with Mickey Mouse ear pattern painting on body, cab and tilt. The washed areas reveal how much lighter a layer of dust could make the paints appear, even allowing for damp making the washed areas look darker. (I.W.M.)

Opposite page, bottom: HQ artillery group at Arnhem, unloading from the first two gliders down. The jeep is in overall khaki drab, but its trailer bears the distinctive Mickey Mouse ear pattern, repeated on the canvas cover. Note the lighter colour of this canvas and its black pattern. (I.W.M.)

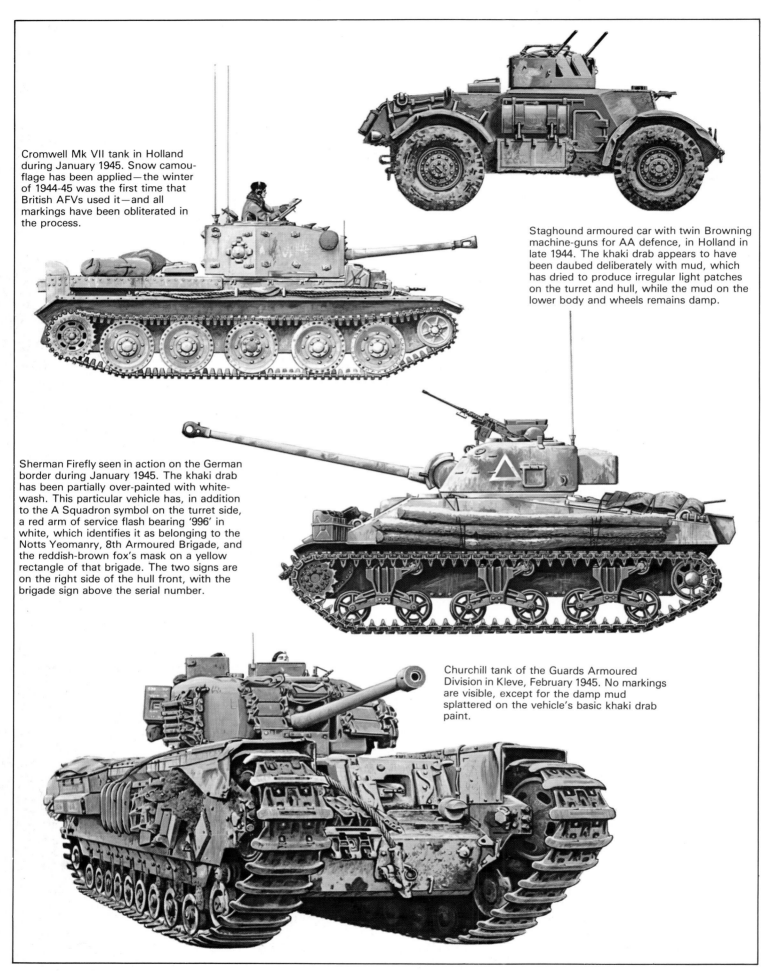

Cromwell Mk VII tank in Holland during January 1945. Snow camouflage has been applied—the winter of 1944-45 was the first time that British AFVs used it—and all markings have been obliterated in the process.

Staghound armoured car with twin Browning machine-guns for AA defence, in Holland in late 1944. The khaki drab appears to have been daubed deliberately with mud, which has dried to produce irregular light patches on the turret and hull, while the mud on the lower body and wheels remains damp.

Sherman Firefly seen in action on the German border during January 1945. The khaki drab has been partially over-painted with whitewash. This particular vehicle has, in addition to the A Squadron symbol on the turret side, a red arm of service flash bearing '996' in white, which identifies it as belonging to the Notts Yeomanry, 8th Armoured Brigade, and the reddish-brown fox's mask on a yellow rectangle of that brigade. The two signs are on the right side of the hull front, with the brigade sign above the serial number.

Churchill tank of the Guards Armoured Division in Kleve, February 1945. No markings are visible, except for the damp mud splattered on the vehicle's basic khaki drab paint.

Above: M7 Priests of 33rd Field Artillery Regiment, June 1944. The vehicles are in fresh khaki drab, except for some dust on the suspension, aided by local foliage (which is already beginning to droop). (I.W.M.)

Right: Typical muddy conditions of AFV suspension, in this case on a Sherman in November 1944. The dead foliage assists in breaking the vehicle's outline and plain colour. (I.W.M.)

applied over khaki drab in only one coat, the black sometimes took on a dark brownish tinge. Canvas tilts were painted before the black patterns were applied, and here the overall colours tended to look a shade or so lighter. On occasion, even the tilts of smaller vehicles such as jeeps, Dukws and utility cars were painted with the Mickey Mouse ear pattern.

The underside of hatches were painted in the overall colour, as were the interiors of open vehicles: closed vehicles, such as tanks and armoured cars, had their interiors painted in a light colour, often white, sometimes, possibly, a very pale blue.

U.S. and Canadian vehicles were issued to British troops in olive drab, and in most cases this overall colour seems to have been retained until either the vehicle needed repainting or it went for repair or modification, when khaki drab was applied. Buffaloes used by the British Army (79th Armoured Division) were, therefore, normally painted olive drab, although some amphibious and wading vehicles were painted in Admiralty light grey for the D-Day landings.

A number of Allied forces can be included under this heading for convenience: namely, the large Canadian forces, the Polish divisions, Netherlands, Belgian and Czech brigades. The Canadian

Top: Priests in action on a ridge overlooking Caen, July 1944. The overall khaki drab is much lightened by dust now. Local foliage in this static position is reaped from the surrounding crops, though the farthest Priest is using a dark net. (I.W.M.)

Middle: A carrier in overall khaki drab, lightened by dust and with corn taken from its immediate surroundings in the vicinity of Fontane-Etoupefour, July 1944. The number and name have been painted freehand on a darker background, which may be the earlier olive green. (I.W.M.)

Left: A Sherman, well-camouflaged with foliage, passes a knocked-out armoured car of the 15th Reconnaissance Regiment at the end of July 1944. Both vehicles have their paint considerably lightened by the prolific dust of that summer. (I.W.M.)

Opposite page, top: Shermans of 7th Armoured Division moving to cut off the Germans escaping from the Hertozen-bosch area, October 1944. Evergreen foliage was popular, but the leading tank has also used a good deal of oak. Note the chalky appearance of some painted areas and the metal exposed on the gun barrel of the first tank. (I.W.M.)

Opposite page, bottom: A Sherman of 8th Armoured Brigade at Issum, March 1945. The tank is camouflaged by a mixture of dead and evergreen foliage, mud and paintwork consisting of dusty and worn khaki drab with some patches of whitewash remaining on the horizontal surfaces. (I.W.M.)

Top: Shermans in Cahagnes, August 1944. The hull and turret of the leading tank are almost completely covered by a mass of chicken wire which, from a distance, has a mossy appearance. Foliage could be thrust into this at will. (I.W.M.)

Left: A Grant CDL as used for the Rhine crossing. Although this mossy camouflage appears perfect, it had little effective value, as it did nothing to break the vehicle's outline or conceal its identity. The suspension is much lightened by dust. (I.W.M.)

Bottom: A command tank showing the chicken wire arrangement in close-up. This particular vehicle belongs to the Coldstream Guards and was photographed in April 1945. Note the dust on the paintwork and rain marks on the side of the box on the glacis. (I.W.M.)

Opposite page, top: A Cullin Hedgerow Device on a Sherman Firefly. Netting has been spread permanently over turret, hull and gun barrel and is partially garnished: foliage could be added as required. The dirt on the road indicates the amount of earth held on the tracks and suspension of tanks, even in summer. (I.W.M.)

Opposite page, bottom: A Sherman of 4th Armoured Brigade being refuelled, late June 1944. The khaki drab of the tank is dusty and heavily stained. Note the squadron and troop signs on the turret (3rd Troop of A Squadron). The lorry has the bold pattern painting of 1944-45 and, because of its dangerous role, has its net permanently rigged. (I.W.M.)

vehicles normally followed the British camouflage patterns; the others were supplied with British or American vehicles, and these were issued in their respective colours and camouflage patterns. The Free French forces fighting with the U.S. Army were issued with all American equipment and, therefore, conformed to the American camouflage colours and system.

The various comments made in Part 1 concerning dust, mud and the daubing of mud on vehicles as an improvised camouflage, all apply equally to British vehicles. Foliage was also used extensively, although the British do not seem to have gone to such lengths as the Americans to provide permanent means of attaching it to their AFVs. Nevertheless, chicken wire was used quite commonly as a means of securing foliage, especially on Shermans. On other types of AFVs, and on some Shermans, the British seem to have shown a preference, or at least an equal regard, for garnished camouflage nets as a means of concealment. Unlike the Americans, they rigged netting permanently to their vehicles, not just on the hull, but also on the turret and gun barrel, with liberal use of dangling hessian tape. Softskins employed nets for static positions, but again, unlike the Americans, also employed them when mobile, normally draped over the body and cab roof. The photographs in this section illustrate this extensive use of nets.

Opposite page, top: A Challenger tank in Holland, October 1944. Wire mesh has been used to hold the evergreen foliage round the turret and gun barrel. Note also the dust and stains on the paintwork. (I.W.M.)

Opposite page, bottom: The tank in the foreground has garnished nets permanently rigged around the turret and on the glacis; the tank destroyers to the right rear have their nets extended along the hull sides. (I.W.M.)

Top: Churchills in France, July 1944. The khaki drab is heavily coated in dust, splotched with oil and other stains, and the turrets have a unique, fine mesh net fitted tightly round the sides; the second tank has a little foliage thrust into this net. (I.W.M.)

Middle: D-Day plus 1. Most of these softskins are painted in the Mickey Mouse ear pattern, and several have their camouflage nets rigged permanently, either fully extended or ready to be so. Note the lightness of the tilts. (I.W.M.)

Right: Shermans moving to the attack east of Caen, mid-July 1944. Hessian tape and corn have been combined here for camouflage, and the lead vehicle also has some sort of grassy material, perhaps complete turves, on the wings. Again, the paintwork is very dusty, especially on the suspension and horizontal surfaces. (I.W.M.)

Opposite page, top: A Cromwell and tank destroyers using canvas with hessian tape 'streamers'. (I.W.M.)

Opposite page, bottom: Cromwells of the 2nd Welsh Guards moving forward south of Escoville, mid-July 1944. These vehicles have sandbags on the glacis and hessian tape meshed round the turret. Note the heavy layer of dust on horizontal surfaces. The markings on the leading tank are (left to right) unit serial number, bridge classification number, squadron tactical sign and Guards Armoured Division formation sign. (I.W.M.)

Top: A Cromwell using the hedge to conceal its hull, the turret outline camouflaged with hessian tape, July 1944. (I.W.M.)

Middle: A Sherman bulldozer in action in Normandy. The vehicle has sandbags on the glacis and is completely covered in heavily garnished net, permanently rigged. (I.W.M.)

Right: M10 tank destroyers at Cahagnes, August 1944. Their hulls and turrets are completely covered by hessian tape. (I.W.M.)

The 1941 Camouflage pamphlet sets out the allocation of nets to vehicles as follows: one 35 × 15ft net for each scout car (to be cut into two halves), two 25 × 12ft nets for each armoured car, one 35 × 15ft net for tanks, two 14 × 14ft nets for lorries up to 30cwt, two 24 × 24ft nets for lorries over 30cwt, and one 14 × 14ft net for cars of all types.

The winter of 1944-45 saw the introduction of snow camouflage on British Army vehicles for the first time in any war. As with the Americans, snow camouflage generally consisted of the rough application of whitewash over all parts of the vehicle except the wheels, and the occasional use of white sheeting. However, 21st Army Group rose to the historic occasion by issuing a Snow Camouflage booklet in January 1945, and it is well worth quoting a few passages to illustrate how the official and actual methods varied.

"34. Use of Whitening Agents. In western Germany and in the Low Countries snow conditions are seldom constant. Rapid thaws may be expected, and snow cover will not necessarily be continuous over a wide area. Moreover, even in deep snow, buildings, woods and other features still provide dark backgrounds. White paint or other whitening agents should not, therefore, be used directly on vehicles and weapons, but only as a means of whitening materials to be put on them.

35. White paint may be used, when practicable, on the underside of any tarpaulins which can be reversed."

Elsewhere the booklet states: "To provide a temporarily effective camouflage material, garnished nets can be dragged in the snow."

A limited quantity of snow camouflage equipment was provided for forward troops and was listed in Appendix A: "*Calico*: supplied in rolls of three foot width. Suitable application, making into patches with strings attached, to be used on artillery or other nets, or for attachment to tank turrets, guns, recce vehicles and for general improvisation. *White Scrim*: supplied in rolls of 100 yards length, three inches wide. For garnishing nets, wire netting, helmet covers, wrapping of gun barrels, small arms and for sniper aids."

Appendix C. listed methods of preparing limewash from rock lime (24 hours) and slaked lime, using salt or powdered glue to obtain a more permanent type of paint. It can be seen that, using only limewash, this snow camouflage was not very durable and would soon begin to reveal patches of the darker colours underneath. The photographs in this section bear this out, and illustrate how the order not to apply paint to vehicles was largely ignored.

Top: A Sherman moving up for an attack near Livry, late July 1944. Tarpaulins have been used all over the tank, but this does nothing to assist in camouflaging the vehicle. (I.W.M.)

Bottom: Application of whitewash in the field for a Humber scout car of 7th Armoured Division, January 1945. This was about the time the 21st Army Group released a booklet stipulating that such painting should not be carried out on vehicles. (I.W.M.)

Opposite page, top: Cromwells in overall whitewash in Dieteren, north of Sittard, January 1945. As with the scout car in the previous photograph, application has been rough but effective. On both tanks, the driver's hatch has the inner face also painted white, though the turret hatches, normally unseen by the enemy at ground level, are still in khaki drab. (I.W.M.)

Opposite page, bottom: Armour accompanying infantry (6th Cameronians) of 52nd Division in an advance from the German border village of Tuddern in mid-January 1945. All vehicles visible have received a good coating of whitewash. The tilts of jeep and lorry in the background are unpainted. (I.W.M.)

National identification and aerial recognition marks

The five-pointed star and similar star within a circle, as described for the U.S. Army, were used as national identification and aerial recognition marks by all British and Allied forces during 1944-45. However, some of the minority forces using British and American equipment also carried a separate national identification symbol. In the case of the Polish forces, this was a white oval bearing 'PL' in black, carried on the front and rear of vehicles. Dutch troops used a yellow lion rampant on a blue field, although this was also the formation sign of the Royal Netherlands Brigade (Princess Irene's.) Free French vehicles were identified by a square or rectangular tricolour device, and French Forces of the Interior by the Cross of Lorraine or merely the initials 'F.F.I.'

Unit identification symbols

All formations down to brigade level were identified by a formation sign, which normally took the form of a badge painted on a coloured background, 8½ inches wide by 9½ inches high. This sign was usually painted on the front and rear of vehicles, most commonly on the left hand side, though there was no hard and fast rule, and the sign might appear on either side or even centrally, and was sometimes combined with the arm of service sign (see below). A selection of signs for the appropriate formations is included. These signs were painted or stencilled on the vehicles after delivery to the unit, as were national identification and aerial recognition marks.

All vehicles also carried a similarly sized arm of service patch, normally painted on

Above: Cleaning the gun of a Sherman after fighting at Schilberg, late January 1945. The whitewash has almost completely worn off this tank. Again, the result is good in the local terrain of dark buildings and trees, with only a light scattering of snow on the ground. (I.W.M.)
Left: A Sherman with 52nd Division at Hongen, January 1945. The thick and rough coat of whitewash is badly broken-up, but the patchy result was good camouflage in the circumstances (there being little snow on the ground) as was the mud on the suspension and lower hull. (I.W.M.)
Opposite page, bottom: A Sherman Firefly of Notts Yeomanry, 8th Armoured Brigade, and carrier of 52nd Division at Tuddern, January 1945. Note the clutter of gear and logs strapped along the hull side. (I.W.M.)

the left side at front and rear, though, as with the formation sign, it might be in any convenient position. These patches identified by colour the type of unit and they were painted on the vehicles before delivery to the unit. The colours were: HQ (including Medical, M.P., Postal and Intelligence units), black; RASC, red over green, divided diagonally top right to bottom left; Signals, white over blue, divided horizontally; Engineers, light blue; REME, blue/yellow/red, divided horizontally; RAOC, blue/red/blue, divided vertically; Royal Artillery, red over blue, divided horizontally; recce regiments, green over blue, divided horizontally; senior Armoured Brigade of Armoured Division and senior Infantry Brigade of Infantry Division, red; junior Armoured Brigade of Armoured Division and 2nd Infantry Brigade of Infantry Division, green; junior Infantry Brigade of Infantry Division, brown.

Formations higher than division had a two inch wide white bar added as a distinguishing mark: Corps, across the top of the patch; Army, across the bottom; Army Group, diagonally top right to bottom left; GHQ, diagonally top left to bottom right. The diagonal bars were 'broken' at the centre where they crossed the unit serial number.

Unit serial numbers

The individual units within a division, or higher formation, were identified by a unit serial number. Because these numbers, combined with the other markings, could reveal the order of battle of the British Army, they were placed on the secret list and many such signs have been obliterated by the censor in wartime photographs.

7th Armoured Div., red jerboa on white field.

11th Armoured Div., black bull with red horns, nostrils and hooves, on a yellow field.

Guards Armoured Div., blue field with red border, bearing a white eye.

79th Armoured Div., black inner border and yellow field with black and white bull's head with red nostrils and horns.

4th Armoured Bde., black jerboa on white disc on black square.

6th Armoured Bde., white shield with blue/red/blue stripe bearing a gold sword overall.

8th Armoured Bde., brown fox's mask on yellow circle.

22nd Armoured Bde., red stag's head on white field.

27th Armoured Bde., blue shield bearing white seahorse with gold shading.

33rd Armoured Bde., green triangle over a black one.

This prevents the listing of all serial numbers used in north-west Europe during 1944-45, but two typical examples have been listed in Tables 6 and 7.

Table 6. Unit serial numbers of British armoured divisions, 1944-45

Unit	Number
Divisional HQ, REME HQ, RASC HQ	40
RA HQ	80
Armoured Recce Regt	43
Armoured Car Regt (Corps Troops)	44
Armoured Brigade HQ	50
3 Armoured Regts	51, 52, 53
Motor Battalion	54
Infantry Brigade HQ	60
3 Infantry Battalions	61, 62, 63
Independent Machine-gun Company	64
2 Field Regts RA	74, 76
Anti-tank Regt	77
Light AA Regt	73
2 Field Squadrons RE	41, 46
Field Park Squadron RE	42
Divisional Bridging Troop	52
Armoured Brigade Company RASC	81
Infantry Brigade Company RASC	83
Divisional Troops Company RASC	84
Transport Company RASC	82
Ordnance Field Park	97
Armoured Brigade Workshop REME	99
Infantry Brigade Workshop REME	100
Light AA Regt Workshop	73
Divisional Signals	—*
Light Field Ambulance	89
Field Ambulance	90
Field Dressing Station	93

*Signals adopt the number of the unit to which they have been attached.

Table 7. Unit serial numbers of 1st Canadian Armoured Brigade (Independent)

Unit	Number	Arm of Service patch
Brigade HQ	172	Blue
11th Armoured Regt	173	Blue
12th Armoured Regt	174	Blue
14th Armoured Regt	175	Blue
Brigade Signals	172	White/blue
1st Armoured Brigade Company	176	Red/green
2nd Light Field Ambulance	169	Black
1st Armoured Brigade Ordnance Field Park	656	Blue/red/blue
1st Armoured Brigade Workshop	99	Blue/yellow/red
1st Tank Troops Workshop	5393	Blue/yellow/red
59th L.A.D. (11th Armoured Regt)	173	Blue/yellow/red
60th L.A.D. (12th Armoured Regt)	174	Blue/yellow/red
61st L.A.D. (14th Armoured Regt)	175	Blue/yellow/red
3rd Provost Section	5075	Black

Tactical signs

The AFVs within an armoured regiment were also identified by tactical signs, usually painted on both sides of the turret, occasionally on the turret rear instead, or, if it were an AFV without a turret, on the hull sides. 'HQ' was represented by a diamond, 'A' Squadron by a triangle, 'B' by a square, 'C' by a circle, and 'D' (if there were a 'D' Squadron) by a vertical rectangle. All except the last were in

Opposite page, top: A German Sd Kfz 251 being re-marked by 5/7 Gordons, January 1945. The Highlander has painted the 51st Highland Division formation sign and is now adding the battalion serial number '62'. The half-track is probably wearing its snow camouflage, rather than dunkel gelb, but this has been roughly applied and has worn off at some edges. The new signs could possibly be in yellow, though this is unlikely. If they are in white, then it is interesting to see the difference between fresh white paint and whitewash that has been exposed to weathering. (I.W.M.)

Opposite page, bottom: A Kfz 1/20 Schwimmwagen captured from 12th S.S. Panzer Division near Cheux, July 1944. The signs of the new owners—the black bull of 11th Armoured Division, Allied star, and unit serial number of the 23rd Hussars (white '51' on red)—have been on for some time, as they are splattered with mud. It is difficult to tell what the men are actually painting, for they appear to be using white paint on the original dunkel grau or olivgrun finish! Note the light colour of the interior. (I.W.M.)

Top: Carriers of the King's Company, 1st Grenadier Guards, in France, July 1944. These vehicles bear the Division's motor battalion serial number on the right wing, bridge classification and squadron tactical sign on the hull front, and Guards Armoured Division formation sign on the left wing. The aerial recognition star is on canvas because the carrier lacked a decent horizontal surface on which to paint the sign. (I.W.M.)

Bottom: A Loyd carrier manned by Dutch troops, September 1944. The lion of the Netherlands is on the left front, and a unit serial number '138' on the green over blue of a recce unit on the near wing. Note the khaki drab finish with black wavy pattern at the top edge, but much lighter wavy pattern at the lower edge: possibly this latter is dark earth paint. All the paintwork is much marked and stained. (I.W.M.)

outline only. Troop numbers (1 to 4) and vehicle letters (A to D) were placed within these signs: '1', '1A', '1B', '1C', '1D'. These signs were in a colour determined by the seniority of the regiment within its armoured brigade: senior regiment, red; 2nd, yellow; 3rd, blue; 4th, green. Regiments which were not attached to an armoured brigade used white.

Royal Artillery vehicles bore a blue patch, about eight inches square, on their front and rear, and sometimes on the cab doors also. Red sections were added for battery identification: for 'RHQ' the top half was red; 1st Battery, top right corner; 2nd, bottom right corner; 3rd, bottom left corner; 4th, top left corner (i.e. in clockwise order). A white letter was superimposed on the red area to identify the individual vehicles within the battery.

It was not common for softskins to carry tactical signs, but transport companies of the RASC quite often used numerals or letters to identify individual vehicles within a company, for convenience in convoy work.

Registration numbers

On softskins, registration numbers were officially painted in white on one side of the bonnet (usually the right, although occasionally they appeared on both sides) and on the tailboard. They were sometimes painted on the cab doors when this made an easier identification area, such as on the AEC Matador. AFVs generally carried the numbers on the hull sides, sometimes repeated on the hull front and rear.

The numbers consisted of a prefix letter, as listed below, which identified the type or function of the vehicle, followed by a four-, five-, six- or seven-figure number which denoted the sequence of issue. Canadian vehicles also carried the prefix letter 'C' (see Table 8).

Table 8. Prefixes to registration numbers

A	Ambulances
C	Motorcycles
E	Engineer vehicles (special purpose vehicles)
F	Armoured cars and some scout cars
L	Lorries over 15cwt
M	Cars and some scout cars
P	Amphibians
S	Self-propelled guns
T	Tanks
V	Vans
X	Trailers
Z	Trucks up to and including 15cwt

Above: Shermans moving up for the final attack on Caen, July 1944. The paintwork on these AFVs is considerably lightened by dust. The large white numbers are call signs used as tactical numbers at regimental level, and the '174' on the rear wing identifies these tanks as belonging to 12th Canadian Armoured Regiment. (I.W.M.)

Right: A truck of Polish I Corps (identified by the white formation sign on the left) with 'PL' national marking. The '70' on red/green (divided the wrong way) identifies the truck as one belonging to an infantry brigade R.A.S.C. company, but it is being used here for wireless instruction. Note the bold camouflage pattern in black. (Sikorski Institute)

Daimler armoured car of the 7th Armoured Division (identified by the red jerboa on a white square) on the Baltic coast of Germany in May 1945. The vehicle is in overall khaki drab, except the underside which is painted black. In addition to the formation sign and bridge classification number, the vehicle bears a serial number ('45') on green over blue, which identifies it as belonging to the armoured recce regiment of that division.

Humber scout car of 11th Armoured Division in Germany, May 1945. The serial number '52' indicates that the vehicle belongs to one of the division's armoured regiments; theoretically, it should appear on a red arm of service flash. The white diamond is the tactical sign for HQ vehicles.

Comet tank of the 2nd Fife and Forfar Yeomanry, 11th Armoured Division, in Germany during May 1945. The tank is in overall khaki drab and carries its markings in the position adopted as standard for most AFVs.

Sherman tank in the Reichswald, February 1945, in the basic khaki drab colour scheme with black pattern painting. On the hull front is the fox's mask of 8th Armoured Brigade and the serial number '994' on a red arm of service flash, which identifies it as belonging to the 4/7th Dragoon Guards.

The German Army

A dark grey colour known as dunkel grau (usually referred to now as panzer grey) had been used as the basic overall camouflage colour on German Army vehicles and equipment since 1939, but the special case of the Afrika Korps, fighting in desert conditions, had led to the introduction of a brownish-yellow (gelb-braun) in that theatre in the spring of 1941, while the vast open plains of Russia, sparse in cover of any form, eventually led to abandonment of dunkel grau as the finishing paint for

vehicles and equipment in early 1943. Dunkel grau had been designed to provide a dark tone which would help vehicles to blend into the shadows cast by buildings and trees: in both the desert and Russia such conditions were normally absent.

Heeres Memorandum (Army Memorandum) No. 181, dated 18 February 1943, standardized the overall basic colour for all vehicles and equipment on all fronts as a deep sand-yellow (dunkel gelb), and from this date all new vehicles were

sprayed in this colour at the factories of production. Any vehicles or items of large equipment in the earlier colours were to be repainted in dunkel gelb as soon as possible, but smaller equipment carried in vehicles, such as tool boxes, radios, etc., was to be left in its original colour until further notice. The existing vehicles and equipment of occupation troops, replacements and reserves, were to be repainted only if these troops were moved to front line areas, and this meant that many of the

Below: A Jagdtiger photographed in the Morsbronn area of France during March 1945. The tank is in overall dunkel gelb with a hand-painted pattern in olivgrun. The cross is in white outline only. (U.S. Army)

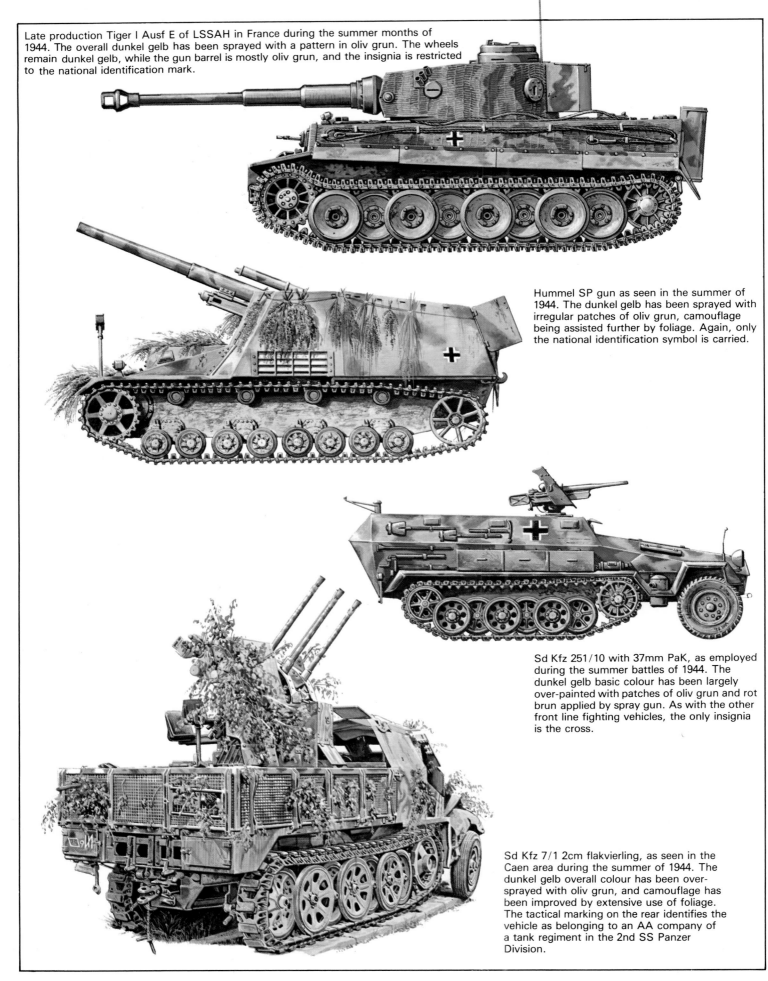

Late production Tiger I Ausf E of LSSAH in France during the summer months of 1944. The overall dunkel gelb has been sprayed with a pattern in oliv grun. The wheels remain dunkel gelb, while the gun barrel is mostly oliv grun, and the insignia is restricted to the national identification mark.

Hummel SP gun as seen in the summer of 1944. The dunkel gelb has been sprayed with irregular patches of oliv grun, camouflage being assisted further by foliage. Again, only the national identification symbol is carried.

Sd Kfz 251/10 with 37mm PaK, as employed during the summer battles of 1944. The dunkel gelb basic colour has been largely over-painted with patches of oliv grun and rot brun applied by spray gun. As with the other front line fighting vehicles, the only insignia is the cross.

Sd Kfz 7/1 2cm flakvierling, as seen in the Caen area during the summer of 1944. The dunkel gelb overall colour has been over-sprayed with oliv grun, and camouflage has been improved by extensive use of foliage. The tactical marking on the rear identifies the vehicle as belonging to an AA company of a tank regiment in the 2nd SS Panzer Division.

Panther Ausf G in France, summer 1944. The tank's basic coat of dunkel gelb has been largely over-painted by hand with oliv gun, except on the road wheels and sprockets.

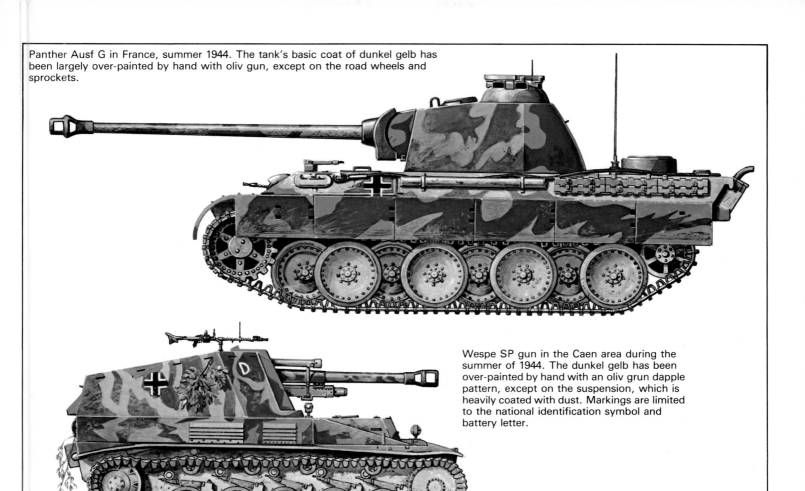

Wespe SP gun in the Caen area during the summer of 1944. The dunkel gelb has been over-painted by hand with an oliv grun dapple pattern, except on the suspension, which is heavily coated with dust. Markings are limited to the national identification symbol and battery letter.

Marder I (PaK 40 on French Lorraine tractor, Sd Kfz 135) as used in France during 1944. The dunkel gelb has been lightly sprayed with a much diluted mix of oliv grun. (The actual vehicle studied had a great deal of dirt on its suspension.) Although not visible here, the cross appears again on the left rear, and there is also a tactical sign in black to the left of centre on the rear.

Opel-Blitz S type 3-ton lorry in France during the summer of 1944. The dunkel gelb has been expertly sprayed with a dapple pattern in oliv grun to create an effective camouflage for wooded areas. The legend on the cab door indicates weight of vehicle and loads carried.

rear area troops, such as the occupation troops in France and the Low Countries, did not repaint their vehicles and equipment but kept dunkel grau as the overall colour. Another Heeres Memorandum (No. 322, issued 11 October 1943) ordered that engineers' bridging materials and landing craft were also to be left in dunkel grau.

The situation is confused more by the mention in some official sources of the dunkel grau scheme being reintroduced in late 1944 for front line armour, yet there is virtually no photographic evidence of such a step: of all the vehicles taken to the Aberdeen Proving Ground after the war, including dozens of Royal Tigers, Panthers, Panzer IVs etc., all are in the dunkel gelb. So far as is known, the only dark colour widely used in north-west Europe on German vehicles was the vert armée employed on some of the SP guns built by Renault, or the Czech three-tone scheme used on most Hetzers built by Skoda and CKD (see later, under ambush pattern.) It has been suggested that a shortage of dunkel gelb led to the use of old stocks of dunkel grau, or that the reintroduction of dunkel grau was an attempt to combat the overwhelming air superiority of the Allies and to make full use of the terrain of north-west Europe, the dunkel grau rendering vehicles much

Opposite page, top: A Jagdtiger at Obernetphen, Germany, in April 1945, painted in overall dunkel gelb. Note how dust and wear have produced gradations of the overall colour. (U.S. Army)

Opposite page, bottom: A Panzerkampfwagen IV captured by 101st Airborne Division at Bastogne. The tank's armour is heavily reinforced with track plates; these, together with dust and mud, make it difficult to judge the colour of the original paintwork which seems, on the turret at least, to have been olivgrun. (U.S. Army)

Top: A Hummel captured near Wurzen, Germany, in April 1945. A bold olivgrun pattern has been applied over the dunkel gelb, and the remains of foliage camouflage can be seen. Note the light colour of the driver's vision port. (U.S. Army)

Middle: A late production Jagdpanzer IV with 7.5cm StuK 42L/70 gun, knocked out in Uekerath, Germany, March 1945. The dunkel gelb has been heavily over-sprayed with olivgrun. Again, foliage has also been used. (U.S. Army)

Bottom: A Wirbelwind Flakpanzer IV near Xertigny, France, in September 1944. The AFV has been sprayed extensively with olivgrun and rotbraun, though some of the original dunkel gelb still shows at the rear and on the suspension, despite a layer of dust. (U.S. Army)

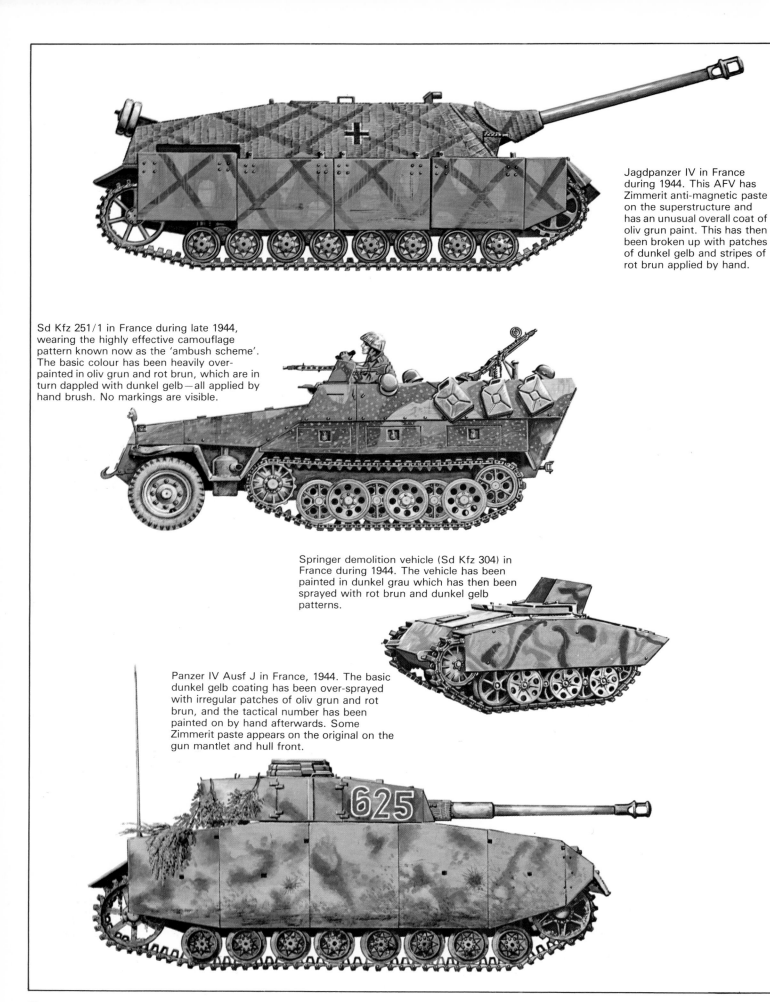

Jagdpanzer IV in France during 1944. This AFV has Zimmerit anti-magnetic paste on the superstructure and has an unusual overall coat of oliv grun paint. This has then been broken up with patches of dunkel gelb and stripes of rot brun applied by hand.

Sd Kfz 251/1 in France during late 1944, wearing the highly effective camouflage pattern known now as the 'ambush scheme'. The basic colour has been heavily over-painted in oliv grun and rot brun, which are in turn dappled with dunkel gelb—all applied by hand brush. No markings are visible.

Springer demolition vehicle (Sd Kfz 304) in France during 1944. The vehicle has been painted in dunkel grau which has then been sprayed with rot brun and dunkel gelb patterns.

Panzer IV Ausf J in France, 1944. The basic dunkel gelb coating has been over-sprayed with irregular patches of oliv grun and rot brun, and the tactical number has been painted on by hand afterwards. Some Zimmerit paste appears on the original on the gun mantlet and hull front.

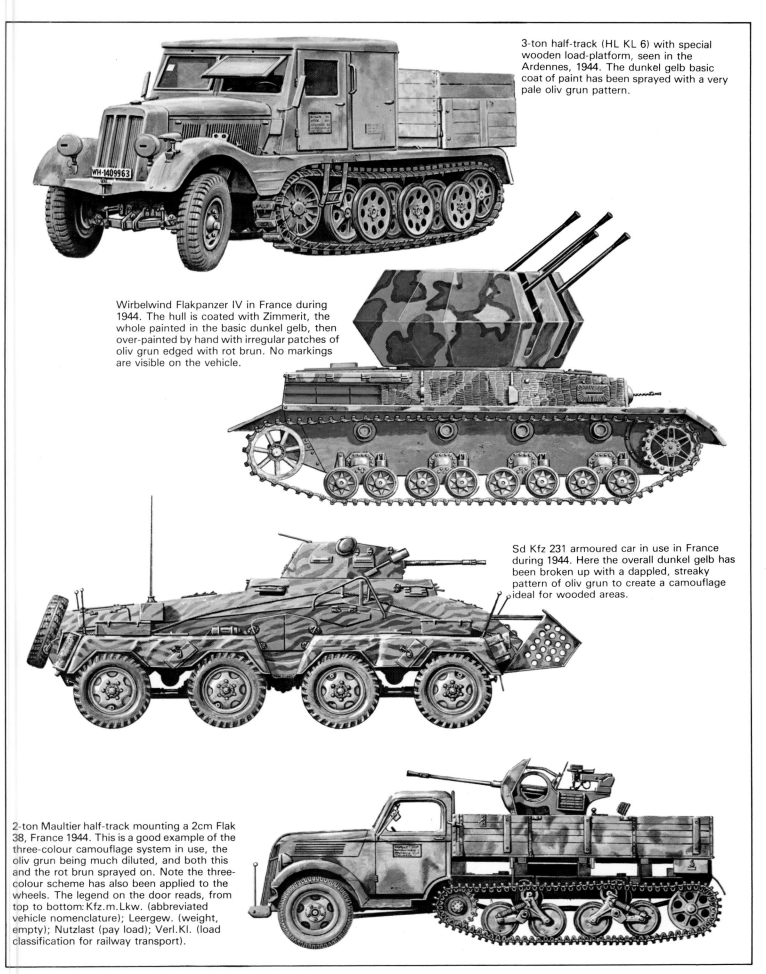

3-ton half-track (HL KL 6) with special wooden load-platform, seen in the Ardennes, 1944. The dunkel gelb basic coat of paint has been sprayed with a very pale oliv grun pattern.

Wirbelwind Flakpanzer IV in France during 1944. The hull is coated with Zimmerit, the whole painted in the basic dunkel gelb, then over-painted by hand with irregular patches of oliv grun edged with rot brun. No markings are visible on the vehicle.

Sd Kfz 231 armoured car in use in France during 1944. Here the overall dunkel gelb has been broken up with a dappled, streaky pattern of oliv grun to create a camouflage ideal for wooded areas.

2-ton Maultier half-track mounting a 2cm Flak 38, France 1944. This is a good example of the three-colour camouflage system in use, the oliv grun being much diluted, and both this and the rot brun sprayed on. Note the three-colour scheme has also been applied to the wheels. The legend on the door reads, from top to bottom: Kfz.m.Lkw. (abbreviated vehicle nomenclature); Leergew. (weight, empty); Nutzlast (pay load); Verl.Kl. (load classification for railway transport).

Left: A Kettenkraftrad being used by the U.S. 506th Parachute Infantry at Carentan, France, in June 1944. The original dunkel gelb is very clear here, with a finely sprayed dapple pattern in olivgrun. (U.S. Army)

Below: A Panther Ausf G near Cleryaux, Luxembourg, during February 1945. A bold, sprayed pattern has been applied in olivgrun over the dunkel gelb; the gloss effect on some surfaces is unusual, even if due to the rain. Note the position and style of the cross and tactical number. (U.S. Army)

less conspicuous from the air and enabling them to use the shadows of buildings, trees and high hedges to maximum advantage. We cannot now tell what happened, but extensive research by Bruce Culver, who has combed through thousands of photographs and talked to German veterans, has shown that the basic colour for German armour in north-west Europe was almost entirely dunkel gelb and the only dunkel grau vehicles for which there is any substantive evidence are test vehicles at some of the works, such as Henschel and M.A.N.: one can only assume that these isolated examples have led earlier writers to claim dunkel grau as the basic colour for many more vehicles than was actually so.

Vehicle colours and markings are difficult subjects, about which it is impossible to be dogmatic. The German Army of 1944-45 was in no position to expend time and energy ensuring all vehicles conformed to official instructions. Dunkel gelb was by far the most common overall colour during the 1944-45 period, but there were indubitably many softskins and artillery pieces, originally belonging to the troops occupying the Low Countries and France, which had remained in their original dunkel grau. Beyond such generalisations, it is not possible to say which vehicles were in dunkel gelb and which were in dunkel grau.

The memorandum of February 1943 also introduced a new camouflage pattern painting system using two other colours, olive green (oliv grun, a colour already in use by the Luftwaffe for ground installations) and a chestnut or reddish-brown (rotbraun.) This was the most sophisticated camouflage painting system so far devised and was to revolutionize the art: many modern armies now employ very similar systems. Its strength lay in the fact

Top: An RSO tractor in Dasburg, Germany, February 1945. The overall coat of paint appears too dark to be dunkel gelb, but this may be because the pattern sprayed over it is so heavy. Alternatively, it is possible it has been sprayed with both olivgrun (masking almost all the dunkel gelb) and the darker pattern is rotbraun. (U.S. Army)

Middle: An 8.8cm gun near Dulman, Germany, March 1945, camouflaged with foliage and a small, brush-applied pattern in olivgrun over the dunkel gelb. (U.S. Army)

Bottom: An Sd Kfz 231 amidst the ruins of St. Lô, July 1944. Despite the damage, it is possible to see the pattern of olivgrun applied irregularly over the dunkel gelb. (U.S. Army)

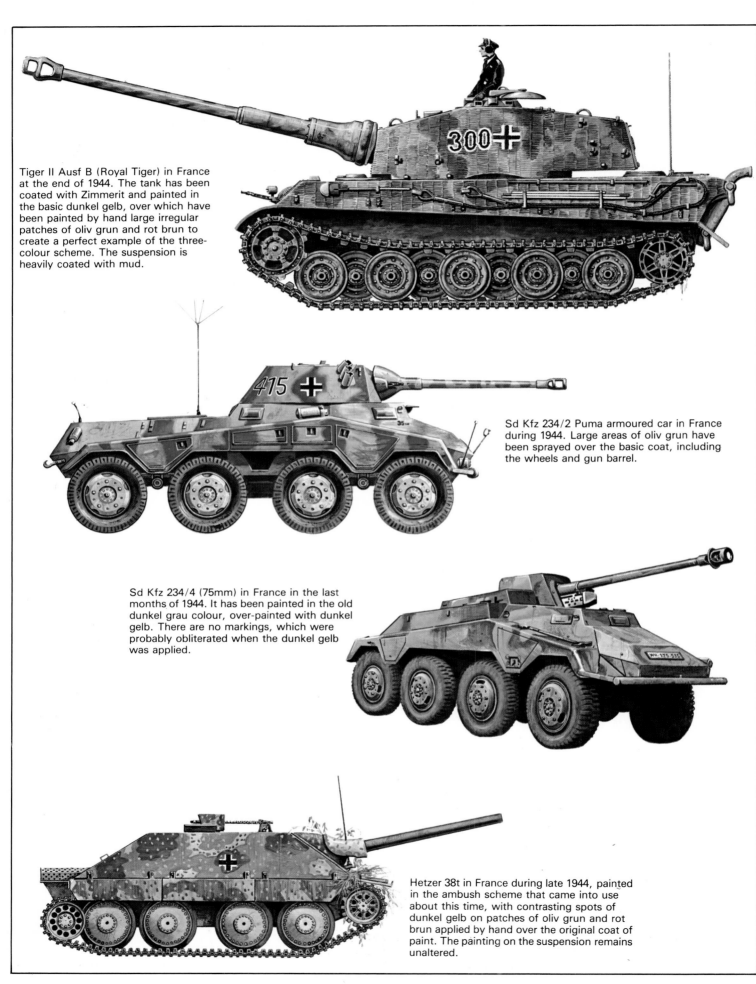

Tiger II Ausf B (Royal Tiger) in France at the end of 1944. The tank has been coated with Zimmerit and painted in the basic dunkel gelb, over which have been painted by hand large irregular patches of oliv grun and rot brun to create a perfect example of the three-colour scheme. The suspension is heavily coated with mud.

Sd Kfz 234/2 Puma armoured car in France during 1944. Large areas of oliv grun have been sprayed over the basic coat, including the wheels and gun barrel.

Sd Kfz 234/4 (75mm) in France in the last months of 1944. It has been painted in the old dunkel grau colour, over-painted with dunkel gelb. There are no markings, which were probably obliterated when the dunkel gelb was applied.

Hetzer 38t in France during late 1944, painted in the ambush scheme that came into use about this time, with contrasting spots of dunkel gelb on patches of oliv grun and rot brun applied by hand over the original coat of paint. The painting on the suspension remains unaltered.

Jagdpanther Ausf G in France towards the end of 1944, painted in the ambush scheme but in this case with the oliv grun and rot brun patches sprayed on. The national identification symbol is the only insignia carried.

StuG III Ausf G during the winter of 1944-45, with the overall dunkel gelb mostly concealed by a winter coat of whitewash. Only the national identification symbol has been left uncovered.

Sd Kfz 251/8 ambulance during the winter of 1944-45. The dunkel gelb has been over-sprayed with a pattern of oliv grun, but with the advent of winter the whole has been covered with a criss-cross pattern of white-wash for snow camouflage.

Jagdtiger in the winter of 1944-45. The vehicle's basic dunkel gelb has been affected by the thin layer of oliv grun overall. Other coloration is dirt and other staining.

Top: A Jagdpanzer IV outside Oberpleis in Germany, March 1945, camouflaged with broad bands of olivgrun over the dunkel gelb. Note also the effect of dirt, and obscuring of the tactical number. (U.S. Army)

Middle: An 8.8cm PaK 43 in overall dunkel gelb with a bold 'lobed' pattern in olivgrun painted over. (I.W.M.)

Bottom: A member of the French Forces of the Interior, outside Brest, on a 250c.c. or 350c.c. twin DKW. The overall dunkel gelb with olivgrun pattern painting has also been applied to the panniers. (I.W.M.)

Opposite page, top: An Sd Kfz 251 being used as an ambulance in Chambois, August 1944. The half-track is in overall dunkel gelb with olivgrun sprayed on in irregular long thin streaks. The sign on the rear door is that of the 232nd Infantry Division. (U.S. Army)

Opposite page, bottom: A 7.5cm Sturmgeschutz 40 on Panzerkampfwagen III Ausf F chassis, in overall dunkel gelb with sprayed patches of olivgrun on the side armour, and probably on the hull and turret. (See the gun barrel and hatch rim.) Note the heavy mud on wheels and tracks. (I.W.M.)

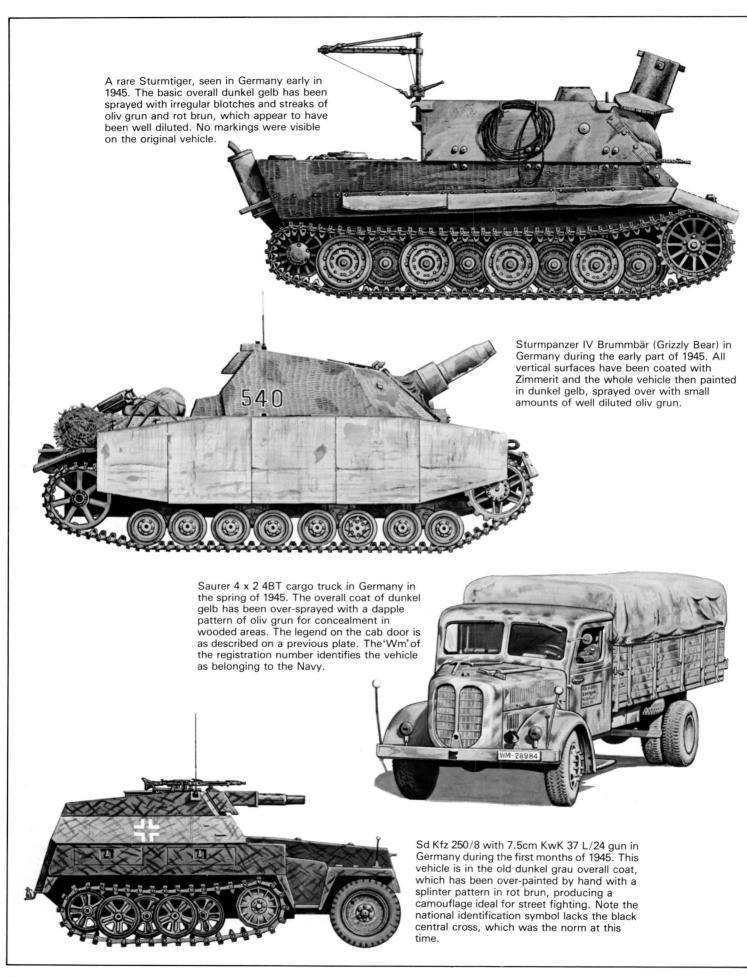

A rare Sturmtiger, seen in Germany early in 1945. The basic overall dunkel gelb has been sprayed with irregular blotches and streaks of oliv grun and rot brun, which appear to have been well diluted. No markings were visible on the original vehicle.

Sturmpanzer IV Brummbär (Grizzly Bear) in Germany during the early part of 1945. All vertical surfaces have been coated with Zimmerit and the whole vehicle then painted in dunkel gelb, sprayed over with small amounts of well diluted oliv grun.

Saurer 4 x 2 4BT cargo truck in Germany in the spring of 1945. The overall coat of dunkel gelb has been over-sprayed with a dapple pattern of oliv grun for concealment in wooded areas. The legend on the cab door is as described on a previous plate. The 'Wm' of the registration number identifies the vehicle as belonging to the Navy.

Sd Kfz 250/8 with 7.5cm KwK 37 L/24 gun in Germany during the first months of 1945. This vehicle is in the old dunkel grau overall coat, which has been over-painted by hand with a splinter pattern in rot brun, producing a camouflage ideal for street fighting. Note the national identification symbol lacks the black central cross, which was the norm at this time.

that there were no hard and fast patterns or even colour combinations, these decisions being left entirely in the hands of the local field commanders—not at divisional level, but at regimental level or even lower. Thus a group of vehicles could be quickly painted in the pattern most suitable for its current surroundings, whether a change be necessary because of seasonal changes in the foliage, new terrain, or entry into built-up areas.

To make such a complex system possible, each vehicle was issued with a tin of olivgrun, another of rotbraun, and a third of dunkel gelb, to be applied over the basic overall colour. New AFVs were issued to units with two kilogram tins of these paints as part of their equipment, while for vehicles already in service, tables were provided which listed the approximate requirements of each type of vehicle or equipment, so that the correct amounts of paint could be ordered.

Because of the nature of this system, it is not possible to allocate patterns to particular vehicle types or dates, but the photographs and colour plates provide a comprehensive selection of typical examples. Judging by photographs and captured vehicles, rotbraun was used more liberally than olivgrun, though it rarely appeared on its own, usually being used in combination with the green. However, in some cases so much green was applied that it appeared to be the overall colour, the dunkel gelb being reduced to a secondary or pattern paint. Rotbraun, ideal for extensive use in built-up areas, would have been useful in the battles for the major German cities in 1945, but towards the end of the war the short active service life of AFVs, combined with paint shortages and supply problems, meant that many AFVs appeared only in dunkel gelb, and newly-issued vehicles rarely received any paint apart from their factory finishing coat.

The camouflage patterns used varied from overall dapple for wooded areas to 'crazy paving' (i.e. narrow zig-zag lines) in

Top: A wrecked 10.5cm gun in Marigny, July 1944. Gun and carriage are in dunkel gelb with an irregular dappled pattern painted over in olivgrun. (U.S. Army)

Middle: A Panzerkampfwagen IV dug-in to command the Lebisey-Caen road, July 1944. Hull and turret front are coated with Zimmerit, painted in dunkel gelb and sprayed with faint patterns in olivgrun. The patterns on the side armour are different, consisting of almost all olivgrun with dappled patches dunkel gelb and rotbraun. See also next photograph. (I.W.M.)

Bottom: A Panzerkampfwagen IV as above, showing Zimmerit on the hull rear and three-colour pattern painting on the side and turret armour. The cross is black, edged in white, the tactical number (4th vehicle of 3rd Troop, 1st Company, 1st Battalion) stencilled in white. (I.W.M.)

Above: A captured Nebelwerfer, August 1944, in overall dunkel gelb with bold over-painting in olivgrun. Note the lightening of tyres by dirt, and the dried mud on rest of the weapon. Foliage and net, used to further camouflage the weapon, have mostly been removed. (I.W.M.)

Left: A destroyed PaK 43 (L71) south of Caen, August 1944. The gun, including its wheels, is in overall dunkel gelb with a striped pattern in olivgrun. (I.W.M.)

Opposite page, top: A Jagdpanzer IV in overall dunkel gelb with large areas over-painted in olivgrun, the whole spotted with various stains. The cross on the extreme rear of the hull is in a position typical of turretless AFVs. (I.W.M.)

Opposite page, middle: The rear of the Jagdpanzer IV shown above, with the bolt pattern painting sprayed on in dunkel gelb and olivgrun. The small spotting is probably dried mud thrown up by the tracks. (I.W.M.)

Opposite page, bottom: A Jagdpanzer 38(t) Hetzer, which is mostly painted in olivgrun with thin straggling patterns in dunkel gelb and rotbraun. The paintwork is dusty and heavily stained in places. (I.W.M.)

open country, and olivgrun and rotbraun were applied in spots, stripes, splinter patterns, or large lobed areas, according to the commander's whim and the dictates of the terrain: the pattern was not important, its effectiveness was. However, some élite formations, mainly SS and Tiger II detachments, appear to have made an attempt at uniformity of pattern within their own units.

The tin of dunkel gelb was used to overpaint the olivgrun and rotbraun when patterns had to be changed drastically. (Petrol could be used to remove the colours, but the German Army had better uses for its petrol by this date.) All three colours were also used to create patterns on the softskins and equipment which had remained in overall dunkel grau.

The panzerjäger crews seem to have taken greater care than most with the pattern painting, probably because their vehicles were more vulnerable and relied more heavily on camouflage for survival than did the tanks, but also because in late 1944, as the German Army withdrew to organize for the Ardennes offensive, isolated units were left behind to delay the Allies' advance. These vehicles usually took up static positions from which they could command important areas, and their crews spent considerable effort to make them as near invisible as possible. The pattern employed is now called, appropriately, the ambush pattern, and consisted of large spots of olivgrun and rotbraun over dunkel gelb, each of these spots then speckled all over with small spots of the other two colours. This simulated the dappled shadows created by sunlight filtering through foliage and made the vehicles, also camouflaged with branches, almost impossible to detect even at close range. Panthers, Jagdpanthers and Hetzers, in particular, used the ambush pattern.

The olivgrun, rotbraun and dunkel gelb paints were in the form of a thick, shoe polish type of paste, which could be thinned to the desired consistency by the addition of water or petrol. The type of thinner used, and the amount, naturally affected the tone of the paint, and the colours used in the field ranged from extremely dark shades, when the paste was applied crudely and virtually straight from the tin, to very light ones. Thus olivgrun could range from almost black to a light pea green, and rotbraun from a deep maroon shade to a light brick red.

The method of application also affected the tone of the colours. Tanks and other heavy vehicles were officially issued with a small spray gun as part of their equipment, the compressor run off the vehicle's engine, but in practice few front line vehicles had a spray gun, and rarely used it

if they had. However, some élite tank units did have sprayed patterns, either applied by the crews or by rear echelon repair shops, and in this method of application olivgrun came out as a dark green, which took on a more medium tone when applied over the dunkel gelb, and rotbraun appeared a chocolate colour. The paints could also be applied by hand, using brushes, rags or even brooms for thin mixtures, and the tones varied considerably under these methods of application. The paints were more commonly applied by hand and this gave a hard edge to the patterns, whereas those applied by spray gun had a graded, merging line where two colours met.

This three-colour system should have given perfect camouflage painting, but in practice it did not always do so. There were a number of reasons why. First, and most important, the pastes themselves proved unstable when mixed with water, and even light rain could cause the colours to run together or even wash off completely. This meant that petrol had to be used to obtain a durable finish, but at this time petrol was in very short supply. In north-west Europe most commanders appear to have insisted that petrol be used for a spray application, and generally good results were obtained, but by the very nature of the system, the decision was taken at a low level and some crews used water, oil or dirty petrol, which caused a great variation in appearance and durability. There was also the difficulty of supplying all units with the pastes when petrol, ammunition, food, reinforcements

Opposite page, top: Captured equipment south of Trevières in France, September 1944, including (in the foreground) a Marder I on French 38L chassis, Panthers and a Renault R35 tank hull. The Panthers are coated with Zimmerit, painted dunkel gelb and over-sprayed with olivgrun. The Marder I uses all three colours of the German camouflage system, with the dunkel gelb main coat mostly replaced by olivgrun. (U.S. Army)

Opposite page, bottom: A King Tiger, its turret side pierced by a bazooka shot, in Osterode, Germany, April 1945. The tank shows some dunkel gelb on the glacis, but is mostly in olivgrun, spotted with dunkel gelb. (U.S. Army)

Top: A Jagdpanzer IV, December 1944 (from a captured photograph). This is a good example of the ambush pattern, olivgrun over the dunkel gelb with spots of dunkel gelb over the olivgrun. (U.S. Army)

Middle: Interior of a Panzerkampfwagen IV turret, painted in white. (I.W.M.)

Bottom: A Wespe 10.5cm SP gun with lobed or 'crazy paving' pattern painting in olivgrun over the dunkel gelb. The interior is in dunkel gelb. (Only the cross and name are original German markings on this example, however.) Note the effect of wear and dirt on the paintwork. (I.W.M.)

Above: 15cm StuH 43 L/12 gun on Sturmpanzer IV chassis (Brummbär). The vehicle is completely coated in Zimmerit anti-magnetic paste, which has been factory-sprayed in dunkel gelb. Areas of sprayed olivgrun can also be faintly seen. (I.W.M.)

Left: A Saurer 4 × 2 heavy cargo truck with cab, body and tilt in two-colour dappled pattern painting of dunkel gelb and olivgrun. The registration number indicates that the vehicle belongs to the Kriegsmarine. The following vehicle appears to be in its original dunkel grau. (I.W.M.)

Opposite page, top: A Tiger II Ausf B in Zimmerit, factory-painted in dunkel gelb and sprayed later with patches of olivgrun—see especially the gun barrel, hull and turret sides. (I.W.M.)

Opposite page, bottom left: A late production Jagdpanzer IV with 7.5cm StuK 42 L/70 gun, completely coated with Zimmerit, sprayed with dunkel gelb. Note the different patterns on the Zimmerit in this group of photos. (I.W.M.)

Opposite page, bottom right: A Panther Ausf G with Zimmerit applied even on the rear bins. Painted overall with dunkel gelb, with a pattern sprayed on later in olivgrun. (I.W.M.)

and replacements had a far higher priority, and during the last stages of the war in Germany the shortages of all materials were so critical that almost all new vehicles received only their overall coat of dunkel gelb.

Patterns painted with water-diluted pastes might only last for a few days and would quickly wear off round entry points. Similarly, the sun or rain and frost could blister and crack the best paint finishes. However, mud and dust, oil and petrol stains, all contributed to create a generally indeterminate pattern which in many cases acted as effectively as the paints themselves. On the eastern front, mud was often daubed on vehicles as a natural camouflage, and although the practice was not so widespread in north-west Europe, certainly in late 1944 and early 1945 some examples of this did occur.

The interiors of open vehicles were normally in the overall colour, those of closed vehicles in a very pale buff or white. The inner surfaces of hatches, exposed when the hatches were open, were also painted in the overall colour.

Canvas tilts and tarpaulins were painted in dunkel gelb, and where the three-colour system was employed, it was extended to these surfaces. This also applied to cloth covers supplied for covering windscreens when they were folded down. Windscreens which could not be folded down were partially covered by sticking strips of cloth over them to prevent light reflection.

From early 1943, a light grey plaster known as Zimmerit had been applied to the vertical surfaces of the hulls and turrets of most tanks and assault guns. The paste was applied in the factories before painting, and on most vehicles was 'raked' with a tool resembling a modern adhesive spreader to create a ridged pattern, though a number of criss-crossing patterns were also used. The paste was intended to roughen surfaces and prevent the placing of magnetic anti-tank hollow charges, which had become a serious menace. It was rarely applied to SP guns and APCs. When the Zimmerit was painted, first with dunkel gelb and later (in the field) with olivgrun and rotbraun, the pattern of tiny ridges created thousands of small shadows which made the paint appear darker and irregular, thus creating a camouflage painting which was superior to that applied to smooth surfaces. However, the use of Zimmerit had been largely discontinued by the end of 1944, and it was rarely seen on vehicles produced and issued in 1945.

Allied air superiority made it essential that all vehicles, particularly AFVs, be as well hidden from aerial observation as

possible, and this was achieved primarily by ensuring that all vehicles carried as much local foliage as possible, often held in place by wires rigged round the vehicle (wire mesh on the gun barrels), and, when static, by tarpaulins and camouflage nets as well as vegetation: tanks, in particular, made extensive use of nets during prolonged halts, at assembly points, in ambushes, and when undergoing repairs. This practice of camouflaging all vehicles so that they resembled moving forests was constantly observed from D-Day onwards, and special care was taken to see that all tanks, armoured recce vehicles and armoured artillery on SP mounts were sufficiently disguised to prevent them being picked out from the mass of other vehicles.

In addition, hundreds of camouflaged shelters were built along the roadsides, especially in northern France, so that vehicles could dive for cover when aircraft approached. Where no such shelters existed, vehicles made use of the shadow from roadside hedges and trees, and all movement stopped until the aircraft had passed. In the hedgerow campaign in Normandy, the use of foliage was particularly important, more so than camouflage painting, and frequently vehicles were so heavily covered with foliage that it is now impossible to recognise them in the photographs. The less heavily armoured artillery and SP guns, in particular, relied extensively on foliage for protection and were kept out of open country as much as possible.

Heeres Memorandum No. 1128 of 18 November 1941 had introduced a washable white paint for camouflage purposes in snow conditions on the eastern front, and this paint was available in north-west Europe in fair amounts during the winter of 1944-45. Usually it was applied in some haste and mostly by crude methods—thrown by the bucketful and spread with brooms being a quite common method. This, together with the effects of weather and wear, resulted in most snow camouflaged vehicles having a patchy appearance, with the original paint finish showing through in many places, but this was as good, if not a better camouflage, than the overall white would have been. Tarpaulins and strips of cloth painted white were also used to break vehicle outlines, but a surprisingly large number of vehicles did not make use of any snow camouflage during the Ardennes offensive.

National markings

The national identification mark for all German vehicles was a black cross edged white, but some vehicles carried an earlier type, consisting of just the white outline,

Opposite page, top: A Brummbär 15cm assault howitzer with Zimmerit on the vertical surfaces, the whole vehicle then sprayed with dunkel gelb and small, indistinct and irregular patches of olivgrun applied over this (most prominent on the front). Most of the netting used to assist camouflage has been pulled away. (I.W.M.)

Opposite page, bottom: A Maultier Panzerwerfer, knocked-out in late August 1944. The half-track is in overall dunkel gelb with a dappled pattern sprayed over in olivgrun. Foliage used to help conceal the vehicle has been pulled away. (I.W.M.)

Top: A Tiger II Ausf B in the foreground, during a parade of a newly-equipped Tiger II company in late 1944. The Zimmerit coatings are sprayed overall in dunkel gelb as usual, with large sprayed patches of olivgrun and rotbraun. The tactical number and cross are in black, edged with white. (I.W.M.)

Middle: The remains of two half-tracks, a tank and (foreground) a Volkswagen 82 light car, on the road to Fontainebleau, August 1944. All vehicles appear to have been using foliage, but have been caught in the open. The car is in dunkel gelb with a sprayed pattern in olivgrun. (U.S. Army)

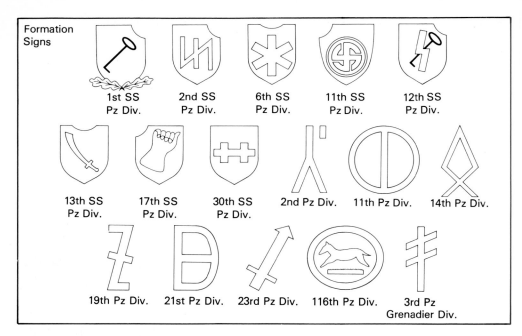

Formation Signs

1st SS Pz Div. · 2nd SS Pz Div. · 6th SS Pz Div. · 11th SS Pz Div. · 12th SS Pz Div.

13th SS Pz Div. · 17th SS Pz Div. · 30th SS Pz Div. · 2nd Pz Div. · 11th Pz Div. · 14th Pz Div.

19th Pz Div. · 21st Pz Div. · 23rd Pz Div. · 116th Pz Div. · 3rd Pz Grenadier Div.

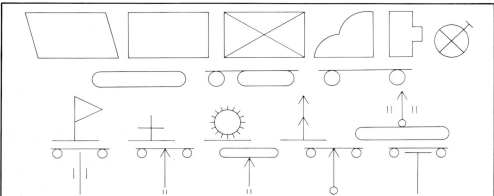

Arm of service symbols: 1st row, Basic symbols for tank units, infantry units, service units, armoured car units, signals units, motor cycle units. 2nd row, Added to the basic symbols to show type of mobility; fully tracked vehicles (tanks, SP guns etc), half tracked or armoured units, wheeled units. 3rd row, Added above the basic symbol to show arm of service; divisional HQ, medical, maintenance, engineers, tracked AA units. 4th row, Added below the basic symbol to show arm of service; motorized guns, motorized howitzers, tracked assault guns, motorized flak AA unit, motorized A/T unit.

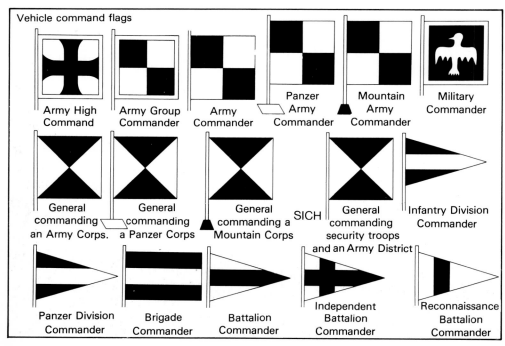

Vehicle command flags

Army High Command · Army Group Commander · Army Commander · Panzer Army Commander · Mountain Army Commander · Military Commander

General commanding an Army Corps. · General commanding a Panzer Corps · General commanding a Mountain Corps · SICH · General commanding security troops and an Army District · Infantry Division Commander

Panzer Division Commander · Brigade Commander · Battalion Commander · Independent Battalion Commander · Reconnaissance Battalion Commander

which had originated during the invasion of France in 1940. These crosses normally appeared on the sides of AFVs and on the turret rear, but during 1944-45, they were frequently obliterated by camouflage painting. Tiger IIs sometimes had the crosses on the turret sides, a position not normally used on other tanks.

An aerial recognition sign was not employed because of the strong air superiority of the Allies.

Unit signs

Divisions were identified by formation signs, a selection of which are illustrated by the line drawings. These were applied in white paint to the most suitable surface at front and rear of the vehicle, most often on the left side.

Arm of service symbols

The arm of service for each unit within a division was indicated by the appropriate combination of the basic symbols illustrated in the accompanying line drawings. The symbols were painted in white, generally on the front left and either left or centre rear. Battery or troop numbers were added to the bottom right of the sign in Arabic numerals.

Arm of service symbols and formation signs were common on softskins, armoured cars and half-tracks, but rarely appeared on the Tigers and other heavy armour.

Tactical marks

Each AFV, including armoured artillery on SP mounts and armoured cars, also bore a tactical number which identified its place within a troop, the troop within a company, the company within a battalion, and the battalion within a regiment. This

was achieved by the first digit indicating the company, the second the troop, and the third the position of the vehicle within the troop. Thus '321' would be the first tank of the 2nd Troop in the 3rd Company. There were two battalions to a panzer regiment, each having four companies, so this tank belonged to the 1st Battalion. Had it carried the number '721' it would have been the first tank of the 2nd Troop in the 7th Company of the 2nd Battalion.

Company HQ vehicles were identified by '01' (company commander), '02' (sergeant major) etc., with the company number in front: '101', '201', '301', etc. At battalion level, the HQ vehicles were also numbered '01' (commander), '02' (adjutant), '03' (ordnance officer), '04' (Signals officer), etc., and preceded by the battalion number, but this time in Roman numerals: 'I01', 'II01', etc. Regimental HQ vehicles bore the same basic numbers, but preceded by the letter 'R': 'R01', 'R02'. Sometimes an HQ tank might carry a number followed by the letter 'B'; this indicated a command tank.

These letters and numbers appeared in a variety of colours, with or without a contrasting edging. The colours were mainly chosen for clarity against camouflage, and in north-west Europe might have been solid black, solid white, white or black or outline only, solid black or red outlined in white, or solid white outlined in black. They were normally carried on the turret sides, and on the hull sides of vehicles without turrets.

Registration numbers consisted of a prefix followed by a number which indicated the sequence of issue. Prefixes were 'WH' for Army, 'WL' for Luftwaffe, and 'WM' for Navy.

Below: An early production Jagdpanzer IV with 7.5cm PaK 39 L/48 gun. The vehicle has all vertical surfaces coated with Zimmerit, painted in a dunkel gelb and olivgrun pattern. The tactical marking ('244') and national cross are in typical positions for turretless AFVs. (I.W.M.)

Bottom: A Maultier ambulance near Hurtgen, Germany, in December 1944. Cab and chassis are dunkel gelb, bonnet and bodywork in white. (U.S. Army)

Bottom, left: A German hospital unit on the road to Allendorf, April 1945, part of the mass of material taken in the Ruhr Pocket. All vehicles are painted white. (U.S. Army)

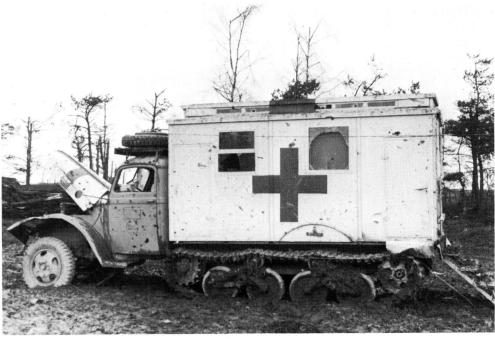

Left: A 2cm Flak on Zugkraftwagen eight-ton half-track in dunkel gelb and olivgrun sprayed pattern, backed up by foliage. The lozenge and 'AA' symbols on the rear indicate that this vehicle belongs to the AA Company of a tank regiment, the number '9' indicating the battery number. The divisional sign is that of the 2nd S.S. Panzer Division originally stationed near Toulouse, but ordered to the Caen area after the D-Day landings and later switched to halt the U.S. breakout. (I.W.M.)

Top: A tractor abandoned by the Germans during the winter of 1944-45. It has been painted white, but the original dunkel gelb shows where the snow camouflage has worn off. (U.S. Army)

Bottom: An Sd Kfz 234/2 Puma armoured car in overall dunkel gelb with irregular sprayed patterns in olivgrun. The cross on the turret is followed by the tactical number '1111' indicating this vehicle was the first in the 1st Troop of the 11th Company. This was an unusual number and occurred only in Panzer Grenadier or S.S. divisions where infantry regiments had extra heavy companies, creating '10' and '11' company numbers. The number is abbreviated to '11' when repeated on the sides. (I.W.M.)

Top: A Panther Ausf A in Zimmerit with dunkel gelb and olivgrun sprayed pattern painting. The national cross, in black edged with white, appears on the rear and the extreme front end of the hull side, an unusual position. The remains of the tactical number ('424') may be seen on the turret rear; it is repeated on the turret sides. (I.W.M.)

Bottom: A Panther Ausf G in Zimmerit with dunkel gelb and olivgrun sprayed pattern. The tactical numbers on the turret (over an earlier one, possibly '123') are black, edged in white, and show the tank to be the eighth vehicle of HQ, 3rd Company, 1st Battalion. The national cross appears in a rare position, just visible at the extreme angled end of the hull side. (I.W.M.)